STRUCTURE, FUNCTION AND PURPOSE

.

STRUCTURE, FUNCTION AND PURPOSE

An Inquiry into the Concepts and Methods
of Biology from the Viewpoint of Time

By ADRIAN C. MOULYN, M. D.

With a Foreword by
YERVANT H. KRIKORIAN

IAP

THE LIBERAL ARTS PRESS

NEW YORK

Published at 153 West 72nd Street, New York 23, N. Y.

Printed in the United States of America

LIFE, PURPOSE AND CAUSALITY

A FOREWORD BY YERVANT H. KRIKORIAN

The problem in *Structure, Function and Purpose* with which Dr. Moulyn is concerned involves issues that have a long history in Western thought, going at least as far back as 2000 years to the time of Democritus and Aristotle. The issues in question have been of central importance in the history of philosophy. To mention but a few philosophers who have struggled with them— Spinoza, Leibniz, and Kant stand out in the philosophy of the past, and Bergson, Dewey, and Whitehead in recent philosophy. They are issues that lie at the borderline between science and philosophy. Yet they are not only of theoretical interest, but vitally relevant to one's ethics and religion and general outlook.

What, then, are these issues with which Dr. Moulyn's discussion is concerned? First, there is the important question of the meaning of terms like structure, function, causality, and purpose as they are used in everyday life and more specifically in biology, psychology, and the social sciences. These terms are highly ambiguous. Dr. Moulyn, with his love of clarity and his talent for analysis, formulates precise definitions of these and similar terms. And, again, there is the question of the applicability of these terms. To what extent and to what areas of experience do they apply? Dr. Moulyn has some interesting things to say in this connection. Finally, there is the over-all philosophic issue of the relation between causality and purpose. Are causal and purposive explanations compatible?

To the question of the relation between causality and purpose which underlies Dr. Moulyn's discussion, there are various answers. The extreme, monistic views are those of the mechanist and of the panpsychist. The mechanist, from Democritus to Jacques Loeb, as Dr. Moulyn rightly says, postulates "the existence of mechanical movement only," he "uses the causal princi-

v

ple," he "admits only quantitative data." From this point of view "purposive movement is a complex variety of mechanical movement." The panpsychist, from Leibniz to Whitehead, argues, in the words of Ward, that "there are no things wholly inert, devoid of all internal springs of action, and only mechanically related to each other."

The monistic views have eminent representatives and strong intellectual appeal. For the mechanist, as Dr. Moulyn points out, all differences in nature are merely varieties of mechanical movement, whereas for the panpsychist they are due merely to the complex variety of the conscious process. Monistic views emphasize the continuity and simplicity of nature. Those who disagree with the monists maintain that they ignore the basic discontinuities or schisms in nature.

Dr. Moulyn rejects the monistic views and advocates a dualistic philosophy. According to him, "inherent schisms exist in reality which cannot be explained away." He therefore asserts, "I for one cannot see any other solution than dualistic explanations of the behavior of man and of higher animals." From his point of view certain biological activities cannot be fully understood in terms of physical causality; they require the purposive explanation.

Yet the dualism Dr. Moulyn defends is of a highly individual type. Most dualists draw a sharp distinction between living and nonliving things, and classify all aspects of living beings as teleological. H. Driesch, for example, would claim that the form, growth, and action of the living organism are something more than mechanism. This something he believes to be a nonperceptible, nonmechanical agency, such as entelechy, and is supposed to solve the obscure problems of biology. "It is my firm conviction," Driesch writes, "that we cannot avoid the admission of vitalistic automatic agents, possessing no experience, i.e., no 'secondary' faculties, and yet endowed with *specific* knowing and willing." Most biologists think, and Dr. Moulyn would join them, that this firm conviction of Driesch solves the difficulties of biology verbally, but actually clarifies none. Dr. Moulyn's dualism is not the biological vitalism of Driesch, though, if I understand him correctly, it has vitalistic implications in the field of psychology. For Dr. Moulyn the structure, the function, the organs, the nervous

system, the growth and most of the actions of the living organism must be described in strictly causal terms. Purpose has sig-
nificance, but it has "a very limited applicability"; it is not a
ubiquitous concept like structure and function. It is applicable
only to human actions and probably to certain actions of the
higher animals.

The reason for the limitation of purpose lies in Dr. Moulyn's
interpretation of the idea of purpose. He finds the difference between causal and purposive action to lie in different notions of
time: objective time and subjective time. Objective time, for him,
is expressed in terms of space; it consists of intervals and punctiform instants which delimit intervals. Subjective time consists of
a past fringe, a present with duration, and a future fringe. It is in
subjective time that one finds the meaning of purpose. In purposive striving one "synthesizes future and past in the present.
This is the characteristic time structure of purposive phenomena
which sets them apart from mechanical movement." And introspection is the means to insight into our own and other people's
purposive activities and into the purposive life of some animals.
Dr. Moulyn's views on purpose and on time remind one of Bergson's *temps durée*. He provides us with fascinating illustrations of
purposive striving in various human activities, including the
musical experience and such experiences as are encountered by
the psychiatrist.

Some may regard Dr. Moulyn's dualism as a responsible and
adequate approach to the theoretical issues of biology, while
others may feel uneasy about it. Traditional dualists would like
to carry the notion of purpose much farther down the scale in
biology than he allows; and naturalistic thinkers would like to
get a more unified account of nature than the one he offers. Yet
probably all, with the exception of the extreme mechanists, would
agree with his significant claim that "some living organisms have
both mechanical and teleological aspects." Exactly how these two
aspects of living beings should be stated is one of the most difficult tasks of philosophy. To this issue Dr. Moulyn provides a clear
and brave answer that deserves our careful consideration.

In addition to his distinctive dualism, the book contains enlightening analyses of concepts like structure, function, purpose,

causality, time, and introspection. Most of these analyses have their independent value. As a scientist, and especially as a psychiatrist and a lover of music, he brings rich relevant factual material to the discussion of abstract issues. Sensitive to philosophic issues, he also offers some fruitful perspectives that help to organize biological facts. Dr. Moulyn's book is, in a sense, a bridge between the scientists and the philosophers. It should be of great interest to those who like hard empirical facts, and also to those who delight in flights of theoretical reflections.

CONTENTS

STRUCTURE, FUNCTION AND PURPOSE

CHAPTER ONE

SURVEYING THE PROBLEM

This book challenges the idea that spatial organic structure is purposeful. Its chief aim is to establish the concept of purpose on the basis of the time structure of certain biological phenomena.

I shall set up the contrast: "structure and function versus purpose" by correlating it with the contrast: "objective time versus subjective time." The structure and function of living organisms are correlated with objective time, while purposive vital phenomena are correlated with subjective time. The time structure of vital phenomena not only determines what concepts one must use to describe them—it also dictates what attitude the observer shall take toward his object. Nonpurposive phenomena which occur in objective time are approached with objective methods and an extraspective attitude; purposive phenomena which exist in subjective time must be approached from a subjective, anthropocentric viewpoint and by introspection. The physical sciences can permit themselves the luxury of overlooking the subjective attitude of the scientist because they deal with a-teleological phenomena, but it is of the greatest importance to describe what is going on in the mind of the biologist because he comes across purpose-striving individuals. Thus, an analysis of the basic concepts of biology from the viewpoint of time brings the subjective processes going on within the observer into focus and it clarifies why the concepts of structure and function are infused by teleological elements.

Since purpose is a vague and ill-defined concept, it contaminates the concepts of structure and function, but biologists are not, on the whole, aware of the hybrid nature of their general concepts. I shall try to bring clarity in this situation by correlating structure and function with causality and with objective time, purpose with teleology and with subjective time; our attitude must be objective and extraspective when we study the structure and the function of living organisms, it must be subjective, anthropocentric, and introspective when we study purposive phenomena. By considering the time structure of the object and the attitude of the observer one can determine which concepts must be used in studying the different aspects of living organisms.

The business of defining the concept of purpose comes up against several difficulties. While structure and function are fairly definite and quite ubiquitous concepts throughout biology, purpose has a fluctuating status, since only a small fraction of vital phenomena can be rightfully called purposive. We do observe such phenomena without a shadow of doubt in one area only: man's activities are, on occasion, purposeful and this implies, of course, that not all of man's behavior is purposeful. Man reaches up in the sphere of purpose through some of his activities. But as soon as we leave the human level we are much less certain whether behavior is purposeful or not. Most scientists will agree that the behavior of primates can be purposeful, but the lower one descends on the evolutionary ladder, the more problematical the status of the concept of purpose becomes. The movements of an ameba can be explained fully on the basis of causality alone without any necessity for interpreting its behavior as purposive—Loeb has described its behavior in terms of tropisms. Nevertheless, some scientists will object to such a purely causal explanation that we are dealing here also with living matter and that there is a modicum of purpose-striving in all that lives. Is not all living matter teleologically organized? In fact, is not the teleological character of living organisms precisely what makes up their "living-ness"?

If one looks a little closer at the supposition that all living organisms form one distinct class, one sees that it is a commonsense viewpoint, a viewpoint that has hardly outgrown the thinking of childhood. The child believes most insistently that living organisms strive for a purpose. He identifies himself, uncritically, with all that lives. Now common sense is a direct outgrowth of childhood thinking which has not gone through a period of apprenticeship in the school of critical contemplation. One assumes that all living organisms are teleological entities and, more specifically, that organic structure and function are purposeful. One believes that one has ears for the purpose of hearing, that one has a heart for the purpose of propelling the blood, that the trunk of a tree has the purpose of carrying the branches and that the finest ramifications and the leaves with their stomata have the purpose of facilitating oxygen discharge and carbon dioxide uptake. But then one stumbles upon the so-called waste in nature; billions of seeds of plants and of animals are lost and never reach the goal for which they seem to be destined. A clinging vine seems to use a tree for the purpose of supporting its long tentacles which by themselves fall helplessly to the ground; but the vine proceeds to strangulate the tree and in the end both die. Pathology abounds in examples of so-called dys-teleological events; e.g., a thrombus closes off an inflamed blood vessel, supposedly for the purpose of preventing spread of infection further down the vessel, but suddenly, a small piece of the thrombus lets go, infarction of some vital organ like lung or brain occurs, and the patient may die very suddenly. Such occurrences should put us on our guard; obviously, the teleological conception of organisms comes up against insoluble problems. Besides, the teleological interpretation of structure and function is superfluous. The tree trunk carries the branches: one can simply say that the trunk is the cause that the branches stay up in the air; the structure of twigs and leaves is one set of causes which make gas exchange on a huge scale between air and cells possible, since this structure provides for a tremendous surface of contact. The tree need not be conceived as a teleological entity; therefore, it can be described quite fully in terms of a causal unity.

It is not my aim to eliminate teleology from biology—quite the contrary, it is imperative that the concept of purpose be defined as clearly as possible. The first step toward such a definition is to show that purpose is not a ubiquitous concept like structure and function, but that it has only a very limited applicability. Beyond this negative demarcation one must show positively that purposive phenomena have a specific time structure, a time structure that cannot be explained in terms of organic structure and function. This is the definitive argument against the teleology of structure and function and the first positive step toward establishing purpose as a scientific concept.

In order to construct a concept of purpose which is useful in biology we have to look into the time problem. There are two directly opposite ways of looking at time: one may focus on the subject or on the object. I propose that we try to understand time from the subjective angle because this leads to insight in the concept of purpose. Instead of talking about time relationships in the world of inanimate objects first and then seeing how this knowledge applies to animals and finally to man, I want to use everyday human experience as a base line in order to gain insight in the time problem as it applies to biology, for we have first-hand information in this respect about one organism: we know how we ourselves and our fellowmen exist in time, whereas we only know about the time structure of the behavior of animals indirectly and, so to say, only by proxy. Let me hasten to add that I do not intend to overlook the importance of objective time in biology; I shall strive to integrate these two modalities of time in so far as this is possible.

I want to use an example of daily living for the base line on which to construct the dichotomy: objective time in contrast to subjective time. Let us compare the subjective experience and the overt behavior of two groups of people traveling by train: commuters and noncommuters. The gist of this comparison is that the first group of travelers exists predominantly in objective time, while the other group lives mostly in subjective time. It looks very much as if the commuters move mechanically from point-instant A, where they board the train, to point-instant B, where they leave it. The train ride itself means very little, if anything, to them in terms of subjective experience; they are much more interested in the card game they are playing with their fellow commuters. Time is represented by the stations which float past, time is streaming along "out there," like empty clock time. A commuter who is capable of registering what is going on within himself can remember how he gradually became used to this daily travel, how the emotional coloring of his experience gradually faded out and how he felt more and more as if he were an object moving mechanically with the train. His behavior and his experience is now repetitively the same yesterday, today, and tomorrow, since he allows himself to be moved passively from A to B as if he were moving in objective time. He has, above all, lost the feeling of anticipation of the future of which he was at one time acutely aware.

Some of the occasional travelers behave in an entirely different fashion. Before they board the train they look to see whether the train is coming and when they see the locomotive appearing around the bend of the tracks they are relieved. Nearing their destination they make dead sure that they get off and they go to the exit of the car long before it is necessary. If one of them is going up for an examination, or if he is a musician giving a concert, or if he is applying for a job on which he has had his heart set for a long time, he looks ahead into the future with considerable apprehension, or even with fear and trembling. The future is pulsatingly alive for him. But he not only experiences the threatening character of the future, he carries with him the intimacy and warmth, the protective atmosphere of his home. He is venturing out from the past into the future and if the task which he wants to perform is particularly unpredictable, as, for instance, the success of a concert, he feels painfully torn between a secure past and the challenging, threatening future.

The very essence of subjective time is this tension between past and future. Purposive behavior, which integrates past and future within the present, is an attempt to synthesize this dichotomy.

Let me say a few words about the people who operate the train. This gives us a look from another angle at the contrast between objective time and subjective time. The train operators use clocks in order to measure time. One would hardly think that time measuring is intricate or difficult, but on closer inspection one sees that a number of highly complex mental and physical processes go into it. Whittled down to bare essentials, this is what happens when one measures time: we use clocks to cut up the movement A to B into a number of small movements; these are the movements of the hour, minute, and second hands. Clocks cut up the "streaming of time" into equal intervals because their escapement mechanism interrupts a uniform, circular motion.

The train and the clock start and stop in punctiform instants, therefore one can compare these movements. In measuring time one lays out a large number of short stretches of movement of a clock parallel to a long stretch of movement *A* to *B* and one counts how many of these short stretches go into the long stretch *A* to *B*. This principle is applied regardless of the magnitude of the movement to be measured; it is applied by the physicist and by the physiologist alike—the only difference is in the technical means of time measuring and in the apparatus which one uses. Sheldon expresses similar thoughts in these words:

> Time as measured is the passage from coexistent events to other (later or earlier) coexistent events; the measure is the *number* of intervening events. We select certain simple and brief events which repeat themselves . . . the briefer they are, the more precise is the enumeration.[1]

Mechanical movement starts and stops in punctiform instants; it occurs in objective time. But not all movement is of the mechanical variety. We know of purposive movements which we perform ourselves and we have good reason to believe that some higher animals are capable of purposive acts.

Purposive movements do not start and stop in punctiform instants, nor can one cut them up in stretches delimited by punctiform instants. Purposive movements occur in subjective time, unlike the movement of a train or that of clocks and unlike the vast majority of movements observed in living organisms. Now subjective time cannot be treated in the same way as we treat objective time, because subjective time does not consist of intervals external to each other, delimited by punctiform instants. On the contrary, subjective time contains past and immediate future within a present instant. All three aspects of time interpenetrate each other in a present instant of subjective time. It is hard to understand this paradoxical character of subjective time and I

---

[1] Wilmon H. Sheldon, *God and Polarity* (New Haven: Yale University Press, 1954), p. 591.

shall return to it again and again in several concrete examples taken from everyday living.

How does this analysis of specifically human acts apply to biological phenomena in general? The vast majority of these phenomena occur in objective time, to wit, the mechanical, physical, and chemical aspects of life. The same is true not only of organs isolated by the physiologist in his laboratory, but also of the greater number of movements performed by living beings as they roam freely about in nature. But somewhere in the animal kingdom we come upon a faint foreshadowing of purposive behavior similar to our own, and wherever there is purposive behavior there takes place some modicum, some degree of synthesis of past and future within the present. Here we are confronted with a time structure that differs radically from the manner in which mechanical movements occur in time.

In so far as we study the structure and the functions of living organisms we get along with the concepts of causality and objective time, but in order to describe the purposive behavior of some living organisms we must look at them from the viewpoint of subjective time. It is from this viewpoint that we can define the concept of purpose. Insight into subjective time, or psychological time, based on awareness through introspection of our own purposive movements must underpin the concept of purpose in biology. Starting out from within, with our own subjective experience, we can work from there outward to the time structure of the purposeful behavior of some animals and into the realm of the mechanical, vegetative [2] functions of living organisms in general.

The time structure of organic movement indicates whether or not the concept of purpose is relevant and necessary for the description of such movement. It is a foregone conclusion that

[2] In biology the use of the word "vegetative" is not restricted to plant life. We speak of the "vegetative" functions of animals, such as heart rate, respiration, intestinal peristalsis, etc.—"vegetative . . . designating functions (as metabolism, nutrition, etc.) most directly concerned with the maintenance of life . . . ." *Webster's New International Dictionary, Unabridged* (2nd ed.; Springfield, Mass.: G. & C. Merriam Co., 1949).

plants are incapable of purposive movements, because of their fixed position, but in the case of animals who have a great deal more freedom of movement, this conclusion can be reached only after critical analysis of the time structure of their behavior. On many levels of evolution there simply cannot be a clear-cut decision one way or the other. When one studies life on the lower levels, for instance, the behavior of monocellular organisms, it is obvious that one deals with cause-effect sequences in the before-and-after in objective time. Nordenskiöld points out that Loeb—

> regards, as far as possible, the movements of animals as tropisms caused by external influences; when an animal moves toward the light, there actually takes place through the effect of the light an oxidation of certain elements in the animal, and this causes the movement; other movements again are induced by chemical associations that arise directly in the innermost being of the animal, as, for instance, in the mating flight of insects.[3]

An ameba puts its pseudopods out in response to stimuli of a chemical nature (chemotaxis, Loeb); *after* the stimulus has reached the surface of the ameba it reacts by putting out a pseudopod, which is a clear-cut cause-effect sequence in objective time. On the other hand, and on the highest step of the evolutionary scale, when I put my hand out to get something, I am projecting this activity into the immediate future of subjective time; this behavior is not merely a reaction to the thing out there, it is undoubtedly purposeful behavior and more than a cause-effect sequence. If one describes ameboid movements as a stimulus-response sequence in the before-and-after of objective time, one gives an account of all the observable facts and there is no need to invoke teleological concepts, but a causal explanation of my own purposive movements is incomplete because it overlooks the time structure of these movements.

But what about all the animals in between man and ameba? Certainly the behavior of apes and monkeys is purposive in many instances. A dog seems to strive for a purpose in the immediate future, for instance, when he learns, quite on his own, to open a

[3] Erik Nordenskiöld, *The History of Biology* (New York: Alfred A. Knopf, 1928), p. 605.

door with his paw. But descend a little lower, to birds, and still lower, to fishes, and one becomes more and more doubtful that the behavior of animals on these levels of evolution is purposive. This uncertainty about the concept of purpose leads to several alternatives: organisms are teleologically constituted, they are causally determined action centers, they are both.

1. The behavior of all living organisms is causally determined, there is no need anywhere in the world of living matter to look for purpose. Causality is the exclusive principle of nature; the concept of purpose must be gotten rid of in biology, since it is unnecessary and, moreover, it causes a rent in the unitary cosmic picture that science is erecting. For the monistic causal conception of living organisms purposiveness is make-believe and superstition: when I am now trying to lay my hand on something out there and I think that I am now striving for a goal in the immediate future, I am only fooling myself, because the truth is that the thing out there emanates stimuli to which my nervous system reacts, and these reactions cause muscle contractions, which are processes within the realm of causality. This viewpoint leads to materialism because it is in the final analysis the spatial structure of the nervous system which is the cause of apparently purposive behavior. This trend of thinking is an attempt to construct theories of human and of animal behavior on the basis of the causal principle to the exclusion of teleological concepts. But in getting rid of the concept of purpose, one makes it impossible to describe the specific attributes which make animals different from plants and man different from animals. Such a theory overlooks the essential difference between mechanical movement and purposive behavior, because it does not get the time structure of these two modalities of movement into focus. And from the angle of experience, the exclusion of purpose from the entire field of biology denies our own introspective certainty that we do, on occasion, perform purposive acts.

2. Another solution of the dilemma between causality and teleology is equally extreme: teleology is the most general principle of nature; every phenomenon, whether observed in inanimate objects or in living organisms, bears witness to a grand design

which pervades the universe. This viewpoint is based on intuition, or, as some claim, on revelation. It leads to a conflict between teleology and causality both of which are vying for the supreme role in the affairs of the cosmos, between determinism and freedom of the will, between science and religion. In matters biological this viewpoint makes for a unitary approach throughout biology, since there is no problem from this standpoint as to how structure and function are related to purposive behavior: the *Anlage* [4] for purposive behavior is already laid down in the structure and function of the cell. However, now one has the problem: do plants, for instance, display purposive behavior? Does a sun flower turn its heart toward the sun because it is seeking for something, or could this movement be purely a cause-effect sequence? Certainly an ameba is teleologically constituted from this point of view, which does not hesitate to attribute psychological attributes to cells. But the very omnipresence of purpose makes it impossible to define this concept and to differentiate it from structure and function.

3. Either alternative is too extreme; let us restrict teleology to man. There is no purpose below man, animals are automata, their behavior is causally determined and plants and inanimate objects are causally constituted. This is the Cartesian solution of the problem and it is not satisfactory in biology because higher animals are undoubtedly capable of purposive acts. Moreover, the Cartesian concept of purpose includes only human behavior on the highest spiritual level in order to save freedom of the will, whereas biology needs a down-to-earth concept of purpose which aids in the description of the behavior of animals and which enables one to differentiate between man and animals. This description and this differentiation can be accomplished by analyzing the time structure of various levels of human and of animal activities. These levels compel us to use the concept of causality coupled with objective time and teleology coupled with subjective time.

---

[4] ". . . the first accumulation of cells in an embryo, recognizable as the commencement of a developing part or organ. . . . Bent; inclination, proclivity." (*Webster's New International Dictionary*).

4. The restriction of purposive behavior to man alone is too narrow for the biologist. One must define teleology broadly enough so that it encompasses animal behavior also. The vast majority of movements of living organisms, including the functions of the human organism, are of the mechanical variety, but here and there, now and then, we come across purposive movements. We are absolutely certain about the purposive nature of human behavior; we are also reasonably sure that the behavior of primates is purposive; but lower down the scale of evolution one becomes more and more doubtful as to the purposiveness of organic movements. The decision whether or not a biological phenomenon is purposive depends on an analysis of its time structure. Thus, one ends up with a concept of purpose which does have a ceiling, which is man, but which does not have a definite and clear-cut floor. In other words, some distance below man it becomes difficult and sometimes impossible to say whether organic movement is purposive or not, because the criteria for its occurrence in subjective time or in objective time are not clear-cut. From the viewpoint of time the status of the concept of purpose is vague and ill-defined.

Though unsatisfactory, this situation becomes understandable when one correlates the concept of purpose not only to the time structure of movement but also to the attitude which the observer is obliged to take toward his object. In some cases this attitude is definite and clear-cut; there is no sense in speaking of the purposive movement of inanimate objects because one cannot assume an introspective attitude toward them, nor does one project human attributes upon these objects. I am of a mind to limit purpose-striving to man and higher mammals, but others might feel quite convinced that purposive behavior is observed much lower down the evolutionary ladder. Although the fourth alternative does not allow for razor-sharp delineation of the concept of purpose, it does offer a useful definition which on the highest level does not interfere with the spiritual side of man and which leaves the door open for a description of the purposive acts of animals. It seems to me that the fourth solution is the most satisfactory from every point of view. To exclude teleology from biology does not take our own subjective introspective experience of ourselves as purpose-striving human beings into account; to claim that the structure and function of all living organisms are teleologically organized leaves the concept of purpose utterly vague and undefined. To make a clear line of cleavage and to limit purpose to man alone takes the concept of purpose out of the realm of biology, since it acknowledges only the spiritual, value-related aspects of man. The fourth solution has the advantage that it offers a definition of purposive behavior which is on the one hand useful in the entire field of biology and which, on the other, does not interfere in the least with the conception of man as a spiritual, value-related being.

Ideally, an analysis of the concepts of structure, function, and purpose should be enclosed within the framework of a definition of life. The accepted definition of life is based on the existence of a number of properties: (1) There must be structure of an organic nature: cells, tissues, organs, organisms—a structure which is specific for living beings; (2) metabolism, which comprises anabolism, or the building up of the body cells and tissues, and katabolism, or the breakdown of these structures; during the life span of an individual anabolism and katabolism keep each other in balance; (3) procreation is a universal property of living organisms, either by cell division in lower species, or by sexual procreation; (4) adaptation to the environment, self-preservation and preservation of the species; confusion and intermingling of causal and teleological explanations are rife particularly in this field of biology. All of these attributes of living organisms are absent in inanimate objects, and yet each or several of these attributes may be absent and still we can speak of a living organism. For instance, viruses do not possess cellular structure and yet they behave as if they were living organisms. A lungfish can persist for decades without any signs of metabolism, but placed in water it "comes to life again." In plants, sexual procreation is often superfluous because they form new individuals just as well from the already existing plant or from a shoot. Self-preservation is one of the most dubious attributes of living organisms: there is suicide, protection of the herd by the male animal with danger to itself, fight to the death over a female. In short, no satisfactory definition of life has been given so far.

Take for instance Schrödinger's attempt in this direction:

> . . . the most essential part of a living cell—the chromosome fiber— may suitably be called *an aperiodic crystal*. In physics we have dealt hitherto only with *periodic crystals*. . . . the difference in structure is of the same kind as that between an ordinary wallpaper in which the same pattern is repeated again and again in regular periodicity, and a masterpiece of embroidery, say, a Raphael tapestry, which shows no dull repetition but an elaborate, coherent, meaningful design traced by the great master.[5]

This comparison must put us on our guard against anthropomorphic elements in the physicist's theory of life. Such anthropomorphisms can never wholly be evaded and are present in expositions of physical theories of inanimate objects as well, but here they are offset by the predominating use of the mathematical equation which is the clearest possible expression of the time structure of physical phenomena which happen in objective time. Just as the right and left sides of an equation balance each other quantitatively, just so are the objective past and the objective future symmetric. Schrödinger's thoughts about the place of the organism in the cosmos which proceeds toward a state of maximum entropy, i.e., of maximum chaos, suggest further anthropomorphic thinking because "order" is an exquisitely human idea:

> An organism's astonishing gift of concentrating a "stream of order" on itself and thus escaping the decay into atomic chaos . . . seems to be connected with the presence of the "aperiodic solids," the chromosome molecules which doubtless represent the highest degree of well-ordered atomic association we know of . . .—much higher than the ordinary periodic crystal—in virtue of the individual role every atom and every radical is playing here.[6] . . . the aperiodic crystal forming the hereditary substance, [is] largely withdrawn from the disorder of heat motion.[7]

[5] Erwin Schrödinger, *What is Life?* (New York: The Macmillan Company, 1947), p. 3.
[6] *Ibid.*, p. 77.
[7] *Ibid.*, p. 85.

In the epilogue the trend of thought suddenly takes a most interesting turn: the physicist recognizes the importance of introspection. The question asked at the beginning of this treatise: "How can the events *in space and time* which take place within spatial boundaries of a living organism be accounted for by physics and chemistry?" [8] is answered in two statements:

> (1) My body functions as a pure mechanism according to the Laws of Nature. (2) Yet I know, by incontrovertible, direct experience (introspection) that I am directing its motions, of which I foresee the effects, that may be fateful and all-important, in which case I feel and take full responsibility for them.[9]

This interesting passage points up that the physicist has intuitive insight into the dual nature of certain biological phenomena, but it falls far short of a definition of life.

For the purpose of defining structure, function, and purpose with respect to each other it is not really necessary to define life. Let us follow the example of the physicist who does not ask: "Exactly what is electricity?" but instead, he accepts a homely and old-fashioned definition that goes back to Benjamin Franklin: "If a piece of rubber is brought into contact with a piece of flannel and then separated from it, the rubber will possess a negative charge. If a piece of rubber is brought into contact with a piece of flannel and then separated from it, the flannel will possess a positive charge." [10] The more general question, "What is electricity?" is abandoned and one concentrates on the problem: "What does electricity do?" Let us biologists temporarily shelve the question: "What is a living organism in contradistinction to inanimate objects?" and let us ask instead: "What do living organisms do?" One takes for granted that one understands more or less what life is and one goes on to investigate how different organisms behave.

Two major types of behavior spring to the fore: some organisms behave in an a-purposive fashion and others are capable of

---

[8] *Ibid.*, p. 1.
[9] *Ibid.*, p. 55, "Epilogue."
[10] *Webster's New International Dictionary.*

purpose-striving acts. These two types of behavior suggest that life exists on two levels, on the vegetative and on the purposive levels. Vegetative life exists without purpose-striving, but purposive behavior is always superimposed upon life on the vegetative level. The differentiation of vegetative from purposive vital phenomena invites us to set up two fields of study, "biology in the restricted sense," which analyzes vegetative, a-purposive vital phenomena, and "biology in the wider sense," which investigates purposive organic behavior. Biology in the restricted sense encompasses anatomy, histology, embryology, physiology, biochemistry; these sciences deal with phenomena which exist in space and in objective time, they operate with the concepts of structure and function and they study biological phenomena with extraspective, objective methods. Biology in the wider sense consists of psychiatry, psychology, sociology, and there is much to be said for including anthropology; these sciences deal with phenomena which occur in subjective time, they operate with teleological concepts, and they approach living organisms through introspection and from an anthropocentric viewpoint. Though biology in the wider sense is only a small sector of biology in its entirety, it takes a wider, a more embracing view of its objects than biology in the restricted sense, hence the terminology here proposed. One might say that biology in the restricted sense studies organisms in so far as they belong to the outer world of objects and that biology in the wider sense studies some organisms in so far as they belong to the inner world of the subject. The outer world of objects is characterized by juxtaposition in space and in objective time, while the inner subjective world is characterized by interpenetration in subjective time.

Events which are juxtaposed to each other in space and in time can to a large degree be isloated from each other, they are more or less sufficient unto themselves. The physiologist takes the heart out of an animal, he suspends it in a favorable environment to study its function separate from the rest of the organism. Events which mutually interpenetrate in time cannot be isolated from each other, nor from the organism, nor from the environment without destroying the event and its teleological nature; they are not sufficient unto themselves. The psychiatrist cannot isolate the psychotic or the neurotic symptom from the personality structure of the patient, nor the patient from his social milieu, nor from his historical growth as an individual, and therefore, the psychiatrist's method of studying psychoses or neuroses differs radically from the laboratory methods of the physiologists. The biologist in the wider sense must approach his objects not through extraspection but by introspective methods. These two approaches have to be in consonance with the time structure of the object. Events which interpenetrate in subjective time share some, or many, or all, of the attributes of the observer who, therefore, partakes of the observational setup. The biologist in the restricted sense must remain outside the field of observation, but the biologist in the wider sense cannot take such an aloof, objective attitude. This is one of the major differences between the two divisions of biology. Biology in the restricted sense studies events juxtaposed to each other in objective time; structure and function, causality and objective time, extraspection are the tools with which it operates. Biology in the wider sense studies events which interpenetrate each other and which exist in subjective time, it uses introspection, teleology, and subjective time. Thus one gets two sets of three related opposites:

BIOLOGY IN THE RESTRICTED SENSE	BIOLOGY IN THE WIDER SENSE
1. Structure and Function	1. Purpose
2. Objective Time	2. Subjective Time
3. Extraspection	3. Introspection

The division of biology in two realms where concepts and points of view are in some measure diametrical opposites is apt to raise objections. Why study fishes with one set of concepts and man with another set? This division, this dualism goes against the deep-rooted scientific ideal which strives for an understanding of all of nature with mutually cohering and all-embracing principles. Physical theories, for instance, explain more and more divergent phenomena from one and the same point of view and with identical general concepts due to the breathtaking progress of physics in the last seventy-five years. Listen to what Max Planck said some forty years ago:

> At the present time physics still consists of two great, contrasting realms: mechanics and electrodynamics, or, as one often puts it, physics of matter and physics of ether . . . An appropriate generalizing conception of mechanics could therefore very well include electrodynamics.[11]

The unifying ideal of physics has made such tremendous steps forward that, only forty years after Planck's prediction, mechanics and electrodynamics have become one and the same chapter of theoretical physics; Einstein's most recent mathematic discoveries clinch gravitational fields and electromagnetic fields in one set of differential equations.[12]

Similar unifying tendencies exist in biology and particularly in biochemistry. The metabolism of plants, bacteria, insects, and animals involves the same group of basic substances, namely, proteins, fats, and carbohydrates. The breakdown and resynthesis of these substances follow quite similar routes in the most diverse organisms. Plants and animals use similar enzyme systems, so that they are quite similar chemically. Let me quote, for instance, Meyerhof:

> The classical biology of the nineteenth century gave its main attention to whole organisms and emphasized the differences between species and groups. Biochemists reacted against this specialism: they felt strongly that all living things had much in common and that the essential facts of life could best be studied by investigating the universal structure, function, and substances common to all living creatures.[13]

---

[11] Max Planck, " Die Einheit des Physikalischen Weltbildes," *Physikalische Zeitschrift,* 10:2 (Jan. 15, 1909), 64.

[12] Albert Einstein, "On the Generalized Theory of Gravitation," *Scientific American,* 182 (April, 1950), 13-17.

[13] Otto Meyerhof, "Biochemistry," *Scientific American,* 183 (September, 1950), 63.

Although respiratory processes are quite different and even opposite in plants and in animals, since plants synthesize carbon dioxide into carbohydrates, yet, they have much in common:

> We know that plants require light to produce hydrogen for reducing their carbon compounds, but the formation of these compounds in the first instance is probably brought about by a reaction identical with the reversible assimilation of carbon dioxide in animals.[14]

In so far as man is a metabolizing, functioning organism he has enzyme systems which function quite similarly in other living organisms; the structure and function of human cells is no different, in principle, from that of the cells of animals. Facts and theories concerning cell structure and function are evidence of much unity and promise of more unity to come in biology in the restricted sense. Von Bertalanffy points out the relationships between biology and the physical sciences which are being worked out in modern biology and physics to the mutual benefit of both sciences:

> ... these considerations show that the supposed violation of physical law does not exist, or, more strictly speaking, that it disappears by the extension of physical theory.—Not only must biological theory be based on physics; the new developments show that the biological point of view opens new pathways in physical theory as well.[15]

And yet, notwithstanding all of this eloquent evidence and these inexorable scientific trends, here I make a plea for giving up the unitary ideal in biology in the wider sense. This unitary ideal is unrealistic because, unlike inanimate objects, some living organisms have both mechanical and teleological aspects. Therefore, biologists must approach some living organisms from two different points of view. This dualism, Cassirer explains, was already propounded by Kant:

> Kant . . . asked simply whether it was possible and rational, at one and the same time, to conceive phenomena as obedient to natural law, that is, to refer them to the universal dynamic principle of

[14] *Ibid.*, p. 68.

[15] Ludwig von Bertalanffy, "The Theory of Open Systems in Physics and Biology," *Science*, 3 (January 13, 1950), 27.

causality and to regard them also from the point of view of purpose and organize them and arrange them accordingly.[16]

The biologist in the restricted sense looks at organ structure and function from the causal viewpoint; he isolates organ functions and cell functions from the organism and he breaks these functions up into their components. Isolation and fractionalization establish quantitative facts about vital functions; but, and here is the rub, this very approach sidesteps the organism in so far as it is a purpose-striving entity. Quantitative data, resynthesized, are causal events, but not teleological entities. The biologist in the wider sense who studies purposive behavior and the internal state of man and of some animals, must forego isolation and quantification, he must approach purposive behavior from an anthropocentric viewpoint and by an introspective approach. He uses teleological concepts and the time form of subjective time.

The cell is the point of departure of biology in the restricted sense, while man is the point of departure of biology in the wider sense. Point of departure, approach, concepts, and time forms are imposed by the two types of biological phenomena with which we are confronted. Specifically, it is the time structure of organismic movements which compels one to follow either the isolating, natural scientific, extraspective and objective method, or the introspective, anthropocentric approach.

The dichotomy: "structure and function versus purpose" leads to a dualistic conception of living organisms in contradistinction to the monistic ideal of the physical sciences. However, this monistic ideal is possible in these sciences because they do not come across teleological phenomena. The existence of purpose-striving behavior in some living organisms makes dualism a necessity in biology. Although purposive phenomena are only a minute division of the universe, they require of us, if we wish to understand them in their exceptional nature, to establish specific concepts (purpose), a specific time form (subjective time), and a specific approach (introspection and its "satellites").[17]

[16] Ernst Cassirer, *The Problem of Knowledge,* trans. William H. Woglon and Charles W. Hendel (New Haven: Yale University Press, 1950), p. 121.
[17] Cf. Chapter Seven.

CHAPTER TWO

DEFINING STRUCTURE, FUNCTION
AND PURPOSE

In defining these three concepts one must keep in mind that
there are many interlacing and reciprocal relationships between
them; they can be differentiated from each other by delimiting
structure and function together over against purpose on the basis
of the time structure of biological phenomena.

1. STRUCTURE AND FUNCTION

The structure of living oganisms is not identical with their
shape. Structure is more than the arrangement of cells, tissues,
and organs in space. For instance, the structure of the heart had
been described in quite some detail long before Harvey discovered its function; this discovery changed the conception of the
structure of the heart because now one knew how this structure
is related to its function. Harvey showed that given this spatial
arrangement of hollow muscle, valves, interventricular septum,
vessels entering and leaving the heart, given all these spatial rela
tionships, it follows that the heart must function as a pump. His
insight into the function of the heart tied all the knowledge
about its structure together as he showed that this spatial arrangement imposes a specific function. Structure has connotations beyond mere spatial relationships; it points toward function. *Structure is form, related to function.* Function is expressed in certain
movements of living organisms, namely, mechanical movements.
Mechanical movements occur both in the world of inanimate
objects and in living organisms, and they can be described with
identical methods. The physical sciences conceive the movement
of inanimate objects as a going from a position in a point-instant,
along a stretch of a line, to a position in another point-instant,
and they project movement so conceived on three space co-or-

dinates and on a time co-ordinate. Thus movement is expressed in terms of space because the time factor in mechanical movement can be expressed in terms of space.

The physical principles of describing movement are applied in physiology, for instance, to the function of the heart. The heart moves from one position, diastole, to a second position, systole, and back again to diastole as long as life lasts. These two delimiting positions can be projected upon space and time co-ordinates by suspending the heart and connecting its apex to a writing device which records systole (contraction) and diastole (relaxation) on a kymograph. One needs only two space co-ordinates in this case; while the quantification of the horizontal co-ordinate depends on the speed of the drum of the kymographion, one measures the vertical co-ordinate by a controlled movement of the pen before the actual curve is started. The time co-ordinate is indicated underneath the curve by a time marker. Systole and diastole, projected upon two space co-ordinates and a time co-ordinate, can now be analyzed quantitatively. Such a mechanistic description is possible because heart action is an oscillatory movement between two delimiting positions which can be represented spatially with points and lines.

Function, which is a modality of mechanical movement, is related to structure. *Function is structure changing in objective time.* During systole the heart is at rest for an infinitesimally short instant and it maintains its structural state of contraction; in diastole it maintains its structural state of relaxation for a short instant. The heart functions as a pump because it moves constantly between these two extreme structural states.

A mechanistic description of movement of inanimate objects is complete in itself, but such a description of organic movement is not always complete and final. The anatomist is not satisfied with the description of the structure of the heart in terms of pure spatial relationships, because he wants to relate structure to function. Similarly, after the physiologist has described cardiac function as a mechanical moving between systole and diastole, he seeks to fit this function back into the organism from which he has isolated it. The microcosmos—the circulatory system—has to be understood within the context of the macrocosmos—the intact living organism. However, at this point, teleological connotations slip into the mechanistic conception of the organism as a spatial structure of great complexity. The organism is therefore capable of certain complicated mechanical functions. One goes beyond the causal world into the realm of teleology because we have the innate tendency to see and understand the living organism as a purposeful entity. It is my aim to cleanse the concepts of structure and function from such teleological contamination, and to achieve this end, the concept of purpose must be defined as clearly as possible.

2. PURPOSE

We firmly believe that the heart is structured for the purpose of performing its function; we believe that the function of the heart is purposeful. This intuitive, common-sense belief confuses the three basic biological concepts to the extent that it is quite difficult to disentangle one from the other. The viewpoint that the structure and function of organisms serve a purpose can be challenged by defining the concept of purpose on the basis of the time structure of certain organic movements.

One must distinguish between mechanical organic movements and purpose-striving organic movements because the time structure of these two types of movement differs in essence. Purposive movements are more than functional changes of organic structure and they cannot be described as if they were going from one position to another position in objective time. The time structure of mechanical movement is symmetric, the time structure of purpose-striving movement is asymmetric. In the cardiac cycle, for instance, the past and the future are symmetrically balanced because each succeeding cycle repeats what has just been accomplished in the preceding one. Future equals past in such an oscillatory movement. In contradistinction to this time structure, past and future have entirely different values in purposive movement, because these movements emerge from the known past and they penetrate into the unknown future. Here, past and future are not symmetrically balanced, because there is a weighting in favor of the future. Purposive movement occurs in the here-and-now of subjective time which is an asymmetric time form and which cannot be represented spatially with points and lines. Therefore, purpose-striving movements cannot be projected upon a time-space co-ordinate system; and consequently, biology must develop nonmechanistic methods and principles to study teleological phenomena and above all a specific time form in which these phenomena occur.

How shall we describe, for instance, a man who is crossing a stream by jumping from one stone to another stone? One can describe this movement very well with mechanistic methods if one conceives it as if the man were merely going from one position to the next. One could analyze this movement in a laboratory setting, one could project it on a space-time co-ordinate system, using clocks and measuring rules, one could measure with a calorimeter how much energy the man expends and by correlating myograms with electrocardiograms, with graphs of respiratory rate and pulse rate, one would have a more or less complete mechanistic and quantitative description of this purposive movement. And yet, something is missing, namely, the dynamic, temporal characteristics of purpose-striving movement. The teleological nature of purposive movements and how they unfold in time cannot be described with mechanistic methods, but only by thinking oneself into the activities of the man who is now jumping across the stream.

While he is standing on one stone he is preparing to move toward the stone ahead; he calculates, however roughly, with how much force he will have to hurl himself forward. Then, as he begins to lean forward, getting ready for the take-off, he combines his position on the stone he is now standing on with his movement ahead, and as he next flies through the air, one leg pointing ahead, the other leg just having left its foothold, he is in between a past position he has left and a future position on the stone just ahead of him. When he has found his balance on this stone, he looks back and he feels satisfied with what he has accomplished. The whole, purposeful act cannot be described by the statement:

"The man went from one position on the first stone to the next position on the second stone," because it does not describe the concrete, subjective experience of the individual who performs these movements. The man anticipates the future immediately ahead of him while standing on the first stone, while flying through the air he is suspended, as it were, between his past position and the future position he is aiming for, and in the moment of arrival he looks back to the completed movement in the immediate past. The act of jumping from stone to stone cannot be broken up into smaller segments unless one conceives it with the physicist and with the physiologist as a mechanical going from position to position in objective time. But such a description overlooks the intermeshing of past, present, and future which makes the act into an interpenetrating, indivisible whole. During each phase of the act the man prepares for his future movement, he executes movement in the present and he bases this execution on his immediately preceding past. In other words, purpose-striving movement synthesizes future and past in the present. This is the characteristic time structure of purposive phenomena which sets them apart from mechanical movement such as organic functions.

By analyzing the time structure of our own purposive acts one can show that purpose is not necessarily a metaphysical concept which transcends experience but that purpose is based on the subjective experience of our goal-striving behavior.

Structure is more than the arrangement of parts in space, because it points toward function. Function is changing of these spatial relationships in objective time, and since this time form can be expressed in terms of space, function can be spatially expressed with curves. Thus, function can be anchored upon structure because objective time can be expressed in terms of space. But purpose-striving movements are more than a functional changing of structure in objective time, they are more than a going from position to position, since they occur in subjective time. Now this time form cannot be expressed in terms of space with points and lines, and, therefore, purpose cannot be anchored upon structure. The different time forms of mechanical and of purposive movement compel us to study living organisms from different angles: if one wants to gain insight into their structure and function, one approaches them with an extraspective attitude, one studies them with mechanistic methods, and one searches for quantitative data; if one wants to understand their purposive behavior, one must follow the road of introspection, and this method does not deliver up measurable information. The space-dominated ways of biology in the restricted sense are inappropriate if applied to purposive phenomena. Because biologists are not consciously aware of the contrasting, introspective, and extraspective approaches toward living organisms, the concepts of structure, function, and purpose are ill-defined and vaguely delimited over against each other. It is easier to separate these concepts by analyzing man-made tools than by starting out from living organisms.

3. TOOLS

Physical science studies inanimate objects found in nature only from a causal viewpoint, but we can look at man-made inanimate objects also from a teleological point of view. Tools and machines are inanimate objects *structured* by man so that this structure will *function* in the service of a certain *purpose*.

Let us take a concrete example, for instance, a suspension bridge. It serves the purpose of getting people across a river and it can serve this purpose because it has a certain structure. But the structure in itself, separate from man, is non-purposive; suppose a community builds a bridge and a hundred years later that community is depopulated for one reason or other; the bridge itself has hardly changed, it has still about the same structure as at the time when it was being used for a purpose. Yet, one cannot say any longer that the bridge is purposeful because the relationship between community and bridge has vanished into nothing; it does not serve a purpose, it is now a purposeless structure. One does not have to wait until such a drastic change has taken place to get insight into the relationship between the structure and the function and the purpose of the bridge. One can very well think abstractly of the bridge as an entity sufficient unto itself and devoid of any teleological connotations, much as any inert object can be so conceived. But now one has to approach the bridge with a very specific attitude and one must direct one's attention to the bridge itself, to its component parts, and the relations between these parts. The concrete roadbed supports objects which happen to be on the bridge, beams support the roadbed, vertical cables support the beams, the large horizontal cables from which set upon set of vertical cables are suspended support them in turn, and the big cables ascend toward the huge towers, and finally they are anchored firmly in the earth in massive, concrete blocks on either side of the river. The bridge is a unity of structure and function if one thinks only of the relations between its component parts and if one disregards the fact that the bridge in its entirety serves a purpose within the community. Any man-made tool is a unity of structure and function and a suspension bridge is a most outstanding example of this unity. The bridge as a unity of structural-functional parts is a causally constituted object, and one might as well replace the word "function" by the word "cause"; instead of saying that the vertical cables have the function to support the beams, one can say equally well that they are the cause that the beams are suspended. From this viewpoint the bridge is a closed-off causal unity of structure and function sufficient unto itself.

However, one cannot rest there, because a causal conception of the bridge is unfinished and one-sided, since the bridge is also a teleological entity. Now our attention shifts from the relations between the parts of the bridge to the relation of the bridge in its entirety to the human community, and with this shifting viewpoint structure and function recede into the background and purpose comes to the fore. To sharpen our awareness of the two attitudes which one can take toward the bridge and toward machines in general, let us take a walk across the bridge and look at our leisure at each set of vertical cables, at each set of supporting beams, at each slab of concrete as we move along. One can dissect this dualism of approach into its component attitudes if one becomes conscious that one looks at the units out of which the bridge is built up simultaneously in two different ways: (1) *Stati-*

cally: each slab of concrete, each beam, each set of vertical cables, is a structural-functional unity and a causal link in the entire bridge which supports us; as a unity of structure and function the bridge exists *in space and in objective time;* the lengthening and shortening of the cables, the slight horizontal sway, are clearly a going from position to position between point-instants in objective time; (2) *dynamically:* one slab of concrete, its supporting beams and its set of vertical cables, is a means for our getting to the next slab of concrete on which we shall be walking in the next few seconds; dynamically, we think of ourselves as we are now passing over the bridge in *subjective time.* The dualism of the static-causal and the dynamic-teleological conception of the bridge flows from our ability to look at things under the aspect of space or under the aspect of time. Statically, we think of the bridge as it exists in space, and as it continues to exist in objective time, apart from man; but dynamically we are aware of how we use the bridge to pass over it in time and for a certain purpose. Because we can separate time from space, we can separate structure and function as a cohering twosome from purpose. If we concentrate on the spatial relations within the bridge, we conceive it as a static unity of structure and function in space and in objective time; if we concentrate on the relationships between bridge and man, it becomes a dynamic, purposeful entity under the aspect of subjective time. Structure and function fit into the causal conception of the bridge as it exists in space; consequently, function is a space-determined concept because it depends on structure and it fits into the a-teleological approach under the aspect of space.

Man-made inanimate things remain shut up within themselves in so far as they are structural-functional unities, but as soon as man uses them for a purpose, they point beyond themselves to a teleological relationship with man. Thus, the structure and function of tools and machines point beyond causality toward teleology. Man gives structure to inert matter (he builds steel towers on both sides of a river, he suspends cables from them which support beams, which support a roadbed) so that this structure will function in a certain manner (the bridge supports heavy objects) in view of a purpose (allowing people to cross the river). Tools and machines can be regarded, alternatingly, as causal unities and then again as teleological entities. Insight into the relationship between teleology and causality in the case of tools helps us in understanding the mixed, causal-teleological constitution of some living organisms. The same dualism of static, space-dominated mechanistic approach, and dynamic, time-dominated, telelogical insight exists in biology. This dualism is the basis for the separation of structure and function from purpose.

A rigorous use of language can promote this separation. Man-made inanimate objects *have* structure and function and they *serve* a purpose. Living organisms have structure and function, but they do not have a purpose: some of them *strive for* certain purposes. The verb "to have" expresses the static, fixed, spatial connotations of the concepts of structure and function while the verb "to strive for" stresses the dynamic, flexible, temporal characteristics of the concepts of purpose; the verb "to serve" indicates the teleological relationship between man and the tools he makes.

Since we now have the mutual relationships between structure, function, and purpose in focus, we shall look at these relations in biological contexts. We shall first examine the kidney, next the hand.

4. ORGANS

At first sight it seems as if our organs serve certain purposes, but after closer inspection of the facts it becomes evident that such a teleological interpretation of the structure and function of organs is not really necessary. I shall show that the kidney is an a-teleological unit within the organism and I shall point out how and why teleological elements intermingle with mechanistic explanations of kidney function.

A. The Kidney

The kidney is an excretory organ whose function is to keep the concentration of certain substances in the blood at a constant level, for instance, nonprotein nitrogen, urea, etc. Normal kidney function depends on three processes going on simultaneously: (1) circulation of blood, (2) formation of urine, and (3) transportation of urine outside the body. All of these processes are based on the structure of the kidney.

1. The renal artery steers blood into the substance of the organ where it divides very rapidly into smaller arteries; next, the arteries become arterioles which do not have an elastic coat but only a muscular coat; and finally the arterioles arborize into capillaries which have no muscular coat at all, as they consist merely of thin, flat, endothelial cells. The structure of these cells makes exchange possible between blood and glomeruli of the kidney and between renal tubules and blood.

2. The urine is formed by a double process of filtration and reabsorption according to the generally accepted theory of Cushny.[1] The function of the glomeruli is to filter out certain blood constituents, for instance, nonprotein nitrogen compounds, into the glomerular capsule. The filtrate streams into the tubules which reabsorb water, with the result that the filtrate of low concentration becomes urine of much higher concentration.

3. The third component of kidney function, the collection and transportation of urine, is taken care of by a complex system of collecting tubules which transport the urine to the kidney pelvis, and from there it flows through the ureters to the bladder, where it waits for periodic expulsion to the outside world.

Circulation of blood, formation and transportation of urine, occur simultaneously as three mechanical processes, except that there is a vast difference in magnitude between these three processes; the first and third of these occur on the macroscopic and microscopic levels, while the formation of urine, which is a matter of chemistry, occurs on the atomic-molecular level. Notwithstanding this difference in the magnitude of these processes, one can explain all of the phases of kidney function by means of the concepts of structure and function and the causal principle. The structure of the blood vessels, given the propulsive force of the

---

[1] Charles H. Best and Norman B. Taylor, *The Physiological Basis of Medical Practice* (Baltimore: The Williams & Wilkins Co., 1950), p. 447.

heart, explains circulation of blood through the kidney; the structure of endothelial walls of the glomeruli and the epithelial lining of the convoluted tubules explain how it is possible that chemical substances travel between blood and urine; the structure of the collecting tubules, ureters, bladder explain the transport phase of kidney function. Kidney function can be understood as a mechanical process on the basis of the gross anatomical, the finer microscopic, and the chemical, atomic-molecular structure of the kidney. There is no need to think in teleological terms.

It is interesting to see how physiological theories of kidney function have developed more and more into pure physico-chemical theories during the past hundred years, *pari passu* with the increasing knowledge of these functions. And yet, vitalistic and teleological notions are never wholly gotten rid of; they seem to slip through the mazes of mechanistic theories. Glomerular function is conceived as a chemico-physical process of ultrafiltration, but vital forces are invoked side by side with physical forces to explain the function of the tubules. In 1843, Bowman was

> struck by the design of the glomerulus which seemed to fit it so admirably to the purpose of a filter, he . . . believed that this structure filtered water but that the solids of the urine were secreted by the cells of the tubules.[2]

> Cushny's theory retains filtration by the glomerulus but postulates such a selective reabsorption by the tubules.—A selective process of this nature cannot be explained upon the basis of known physical laws, but entails "vital" activity, i.e., the performance of work by the tubular epithelium. Filtration, on the other hand, is due to blind physical forces. The glomerular membrane plays a passive role performing no work.[3]

The mere mention of the contrast "vital activity" versus "blind force" is evidence that biologists still lean toward nonmechanistic, teleological notions. Glomerular ultrafiltration is quantitatively understood because one can calculate fairly exactly the pressure within and outside the glomerulus and therefore one knows the difference between the two. Blood pressure in the

[2] *Ibid.*, p. 446.
[3] *Ibid.*, p. 447.

glomerular tuft, plus osmotic pressure of blood plasma, are greater than the osmotic pressure of the dilute filtrate, and these "blind physical forces" are adequate to explain filtration quantitatively. But the forces which are involved in reabsorption of water from the filtrate by the tubules are not quantitatively accounted for, and, therefore, there is some leeway to invoke the existence of "vital forces" which are supposed to make up for the deficit of the "blind physical forces." Vitalistic ideas and teleological notions worm their way into mechanistic theories through the imperfections of quantitative knowledge. Clearly, one teeters between two thoughts: if the forces which cause movements of particles of inert matter in the kidney are quantitatively known, one calls them "blind physical forces," and if these forces cannot as yet be measured, one takes refuge behind "vital forces." True, this word is used with much self-consciousness and it is usually put in quotation marks, but it does appear in works on kidney function which are otherwise based on physics and chemistry.

> The modern theory is no more a purely mechanical theory than the secretion hypothesis; the modern theory requires that the tubules withdraw a complex fluid from the glomerular filtrate and this implies that the tubular cells shall be able to create and overcome osmotic pressures of many meters of mercury, and such functions cannot possibly at present be explained in physico-chemical terms. In short, renal function cannot possibly be adequately understood until we possess rather full and detailed knowledge as to the nature and reactions of living protoplasm, its sources and forms of energy, etc., etc.—Whether these "vital" functions are concentrated to the tubular cells or not, i.e., whether the filtration-absorption theory or the secretion theory is correct, we are obviously still very far from being able to form a detailed and adequate view on renal functions. —In short, renal function is according to the secretion theory, due to "vital" processes in both glomeruli and tubules; according to the modern filtration-absorption theory renal function is a combination of glomerular ultrafiltration, and tubular absorption and "vital" processes are consequently confined to the tubules.[4]

Here we see how vitalistic notions are rolled back step by step because we understand renal functions more and more in physico-

[4] Gösta Ekehorn, *On the Principles of Renal Function* (Stockholm: P. A. Norstet & Söner, 1931) p. 480.

chemical terms. Starling's secretion theory postulates vital, non-mechanical forces both in the glomeruli and in the tubules, while Cushny's filtration-absorption theory explains glomerular filtration as the effect of physical forces, all the while retaining a vestige of vitalism in the description of tubular function. One hopes and expects that these vitalistic remnants will be entirely eliminated when more quantitative data about tubular function are collected. "Papers of some 30 years ago . . . [show] how readily scientists assumed 'vital' forces . . . which we nowadays regard as purely chemical or physical." ". . . we have no reason to assume any conditions which cannot ultimately be explained by chemical and physical laws." [5] This statement expresses the conviction that vitalistic notions will be dropped from theories of renal function once our quantitative knowledge of the function of the renal tubules is more complete than it is at present.

The reluctance in accepting vitalistic concepts in theories of kidney function points up a vague feeling that "vital forces" are a blemish on physiological theories. If one postulates that the cells of the kidney tubules are capable of "selective absorption," one assumes tacitly that they select these, rather than other, particles for reabsorption into the tubules. The cell is endowed with foresight, choice; they are supposed to possess mysterious powers that work in opposition to physicochemical forces. The cell carries "vital forces" which oppose "blind" physical forces; therefore, it must possess psychological attributes; the cell is a replica in miniature of the whole human being, of the entire animal. Cells, organs are a *homunculus in homine,* an *animalculum in animale.*

Is it not much better to drop vitalistic notions entirely from theories of organ functions even before our quantitative knowledge is complete? Let us patiently wait for physiology to uncover the "blind" forces which cause water to travel against unfavorable pressure gradients from the tubular lumen into the substance of the tubular cells and thence into the blood stream. "Vital" forces do not fit into the picture of kidney function that physics and chemistry are gradually unfolding. Our lack of quantitative

[5] *Ibid.,* p. 695.

knowledge and our intuitive feeling that organs must function for a certain purpose conspire together to lure us into projecting psychological properties of selection upon organs and cells and to invest them with forces of a mysterious and nonmeasurable nature. Physicochemical theories are contaminated by vague teleological notions because the concept of purpose has not been defined clearly. The teleological interpretation of the functions of cells, tissues, organs, and organisms is progressively being undercut by the increasing quantitative knowledge in the field of biochemistry.

This rollback of teleology by the physicochemical approach makes the status of the concept of purpose increasingly precarious. The trend to eliminate purpose from biology can be stopped by defining purposive movement if one takes the trouble to analyze the time structure of this type of organic behavior. Thus, teleology becomes properly delimited and firmly entrenched in biology. The organ in which purposive motility can be observed most objectively is the human hand.

B. The Hand

Most organs are capable of mechanical movement only, but we do perform purposive movements with our hand; consequently, both types of movement are observed in manual motility which must be described both with mechanistic and with teleological concepts and methods. One can describe the movements of the hand perfectly well with measuring rod, clock, and co-ordinate system if one conceives them as mechanical movement. One can analyze movement in the wrist joint, for instance, by fastening the forearm of an experimental subject to an appropriate supporting stand, then, one connects the wrist with a writing device that registers a curve on a kymograph and if one asks the subject to flex and extend his wrist in a certain plane, one gets a record of these movements which can be measured within the framework of two space co-ordinates and a time co-ordinate.[6] Movements of the wrist joint can be decomposed into alternating flex-

[6] Adrian C. Moulyn, "The Limitations of Mechanistic Methods in the Biological Sciences," *Scientific Monthly*, 71:1 (July, 1950), 45.

ion and extension, and these components, resynthesized, are nothing but mechanical movement. A mechanistic description analyzes movement into its components and resynthesizes the original movement from these components. Mechanical hand and finger movements, such as flexion ⇆ extension, supination ⇆ pronation, go from a position in a point-instant to another position in a point-instant; they can be studied with the same methods that mechanics uses to describe the trajectory of a projectile. This movement is broken down into its components—namely, a horizontal and a vertical one, which, resynthesized, explain the structure of the trajectory of the projectile.

Although it is possible to so describe hand and finger movements, this description is nevertheless incomplete because the hand and the fingers also perform purposive movements, and if one tries to apply mechanistic methods to these movements one hits a snag; the resynthesis of the components established by physiological analysis delivers up mechanical movements, but it goes without saying that such a synthesis does not deliver up the purposive characteristics of some hand and finger movements. It is impossible to apply mechanistic methods to purposive movement because there is a deep-rooted difference between these two modalities of movement. Mechanical movement is a going from position to position in the before-and-after of objective time, while purposive movements synthesize past and future in the present and, what's most important, they project into the immediate future.

Writing is an outstanding example of such a synthesis. Let us concentrate on what one experiences while in the midst of writing a letter or a paper, in order to make a cross section in time, as it were, through this activity. One can discover several temporal facets in such a cross-section: one knows what is now being written, one knows also what has been written so far, and one can foretell what will be written in the moment immediately ahead in the future. While one is busy writing a word in the middle of a sentence, one knows to what extent this sentence is complete and what is yet to come. Writing the present word, the partially finished sentence and the words to be written next are integrated in time. Writing integrates past with future in the present.

Here is an example, taken from typewriting, which illustrates the time structure of purposive movement: transposition of letters is a common but very annoying mistake; a careful analysis of this common mishap gives us insight into the cross-section in time through voluntary movement. In transposition the intended sequence of letters is mixed up; for instance, one wants to write "and," but out comes "nad," or "adn." One can see from this error that the three fingers which type this little word are already in their appropriate positions on the three keys before their turn for action comes up. As one is typing the conjunction "and," the fifth left finger presses down "a," the second right finger has already found its place on the "n," and the third left finger is waiting on "d." Thus, one types first "a," then "n," and finally "d," yet, typing is more than a succession of discrete processes in a before-and-after relationship because the movements of the three fingers interpenetrate in time and they project into the future. And precisely the attributes of interpenetration and projection are absent in mechanical movement.

Toolmaking is another example of goal-striving hand and finger movements. These movements are, biologically speaking, more "primordial" than writing, since they are specific for the human species and they are one of the most important conditions for man's survival in the struggle for existence. Toolmaking is one of the many attributes which separate man from animals. ". . . tools, hunting weapons, and finery . . . are the only possessions of many human tribes living in a primitive state of development. . . . On the other hand, we do not know of any animal which invents and makes tools. Invention and the use of tools . . . are typical attributes of man." [7] The possession of tools makes man's survival possible: he has weapons to make up for his weak teeth and for the lack of claws, he has furs and other clothing to make up for his sparse body hair. The outstanding characteristic

[7] G. Revesz, *The Human Hand* (Amsterdam: N.V. Noord Hollandsche Uitgevers Mij., 1941), p. 57.

of toolmaking movements is that they project into the future. When primitive man carefully knocked little chips off a stone to make an arrowhead, he followed a plan he had in his head and which he projected into the future, a plan which he realized step by step. With each chip that flies off the matrix, this plan comes nearer to its realization. The hand and finger movements which give a predetermined shape to a piece of inert matter are of a protensive nature, in contrast to what happens when a stone gets knocked around in a river; the stone loses chips off its surface here and there and it finally becomes smooth and round, but it will never end up with the shape of an arrowhead or the shape of any other man-made tool. These forces do not operate according to a plan projected into the future, they are "blind" physical forces; their blindness is a blindness-to-the-future. Each movement of the man who is making a tool is polarized, as it were, toward the future, because each of his movements fits into a plan projected into the immediate future. Man is a purpose-striving individual and his manual dexterity expresses this essence most clearly.

Organs such as the heart, the kidney, and the nervous system are structural-functional units which make human life and animal life possible, but these organs do not themselves express man's purpose-striving essence; they are the understructure upon which the superstructure of purposeful movements is grafted. Therefore, one should not call toolmaking, writing, gesticulating "functions" of the hand, since these movements are purposive acts which go beyond the scope of anatomy, physiology, biochemistry, and far beyond the realm of natural science. Here begins the field of biology in the wider sense, and here one needs teleological principles. Organ functions belong to the field of biology in the restricted sense and they can be described with mechanistic methods.

Since manual dexterity is an exclusive prerogative of man, insight into the time structure of movements of the hand is an important step toward a scientific theory of man. Such a theory cannot be mechanistically grounded because when man performs purposive hand and finger movements he lifts himself above the background of structure and function and causality, which make these movements possible, onto the level of teleology. Man transcends the realm of causality when he makes tools, when he writes, when he creates works of art and science, because he recreates, and he reshapes himself into a teleological entity. Manual dexterity is one of the unifying middle realms between the world of causality in objective time and the teleological world in subjective time.

The hand is one of the few organs which exist both on the level of causality, objective time, structure, and function, and which exist also on the level of subjective time and teleology, because we use our hand constantly for specific purposes. Yet, one cannot say that these purposive activities *are* the purpose of the hand; all one can say is that we *use* our hand *for* certain purposes. There are two ways of looking at the hand which stem from two diametrically opposed approaches toward reality: the objective, extraspective approach which uncovers the unity of structure and function as a causal entity in objective time, and the subjective, introspective, anthropocentric approach which gives insight into our purpose-striving acts in subjective time.

The functions of the hand are a network of causes and, like any other causal network, it is never completely understood, since causal connections are multiple, never ending, ever receding into the remote past, and proceeding into the remote, unlimited future. But as a purposive entity the hand exists in an entirely different context in which the relationships are definite and clearly delimited—every purposive hand movement spearheads onto one purpose which polarizes all movements of hand and arm, including the supporting posture of the entire body. All these movements head into one direction, the realization of the intended purpose. Here we have an hierarchical relationship between different movements in different parts of the body which is essentially different from the causal relationship between functions that are described by the biologist in the restricted sense.

5. STRATIFICATION IN TIME

Comparing the three examples of tools, kidney and hand, one can see organization in time on two different levels; we define purpose as interpenetration in time, function as juxtaposition in time. Function belongs to the level of causality and objective time, purpose to the level of teleology and subjective time. This stratification in time is difficult to describe because language is designed to express spatial relationships between useful objects and it does not lend itself to descriptions of our internal states.

The kidney is a structural-functional unit on the level of objective time, causally constituted. Tools exist both on the level of objective and subjective time; they can both help and hinder us in differentiating structure and function from purpose. They can help us in making this differentiation if we learn to look at tools (the bridge, for instance) dynamically as a purposive object and statically as a unity of structure and function. However, if we compare organs with tools, the differentiation of structure and function from purpose is hampered because we inject teleological elements into the conception of organ function which do not belong. We have seen that teleological interpretations are a blemish on physiological theories of kidney function. Comparing organs with tools is particularly confusing in the case of the hand, which has been called the master tool after which man-made tools have been fashioned—stone hammers almost duplicate the circumference of the hand.[8] Comparing organs with tools entices us to see purposiveness in the spatial structure of organs; instead, one should look for the purposiveness of organic movement by asking oneself: "Does this movement occur in objective time or does it occur in subjective time?"

The stratification of the behavior of organisms in time raises the question as to how these two levels are related. These strata are continuously integrated in purpose-striving behavior. How this integration actually takes place is the sum and substance of the psychophysical problem. This is the problem that constantly

[8] *Ibid.*, drawing, p. 61.

harasses the dualist. I for one cannot see any other solution than dualistic explanations of the behavior of man and of higher animals.

As for organs, one should stick to the idea that they are structural-functional, a-teleological units within the organism; they are mechanical action centers, regardless whether the organism within which they function is also, in some instances, a purpose-striving individual. But no organ, including the human hand and including the nervous system, is a purpose-striving entity. Therefore one can study the organs and the functions of man with the same methods as one studies organ functions of animals and of plants. One can go one step further—in so far as man is built up out of cells, he is an animal like all other animals and one can proudly point to important practical applications of this conception of man. A hundred years ago, medicine and surgery consisted of not much more than a hit or miss interference with the body economy, but through the past century they have developed into a skillful guidance of many body mechanisms as the result of a mechanistic conception of organ functions. Many infectious diseases can be successfully combated because we know some of the changes which these invaders cause in the body chemistry. The diabetic patient suffers from a lack of insulin; since the discovery of Banting and Best, we have learned how to prepare insulin from animal pancreas, so that one can restore the diabetic patient's carbohydrate metabolism to nearly normal in the majority of cases. Infant mortality has been reduced, devastating diseases like diphtheria and smallpox have been all but eradicated, and in the past fifty years man has added twenty years to his life expectancy. Sudden loss of blood causes chemical changes in the blood which can be forced back to normal with blood and plasma transfusions which have saved thousands of lives in hospitals and on the battlefields. In so far as man is a physicochemical action center, we can counteract the deviations from the normal with physicochemical means. From this viewpoint man's purpose-striving essence can be disregarded, just as one must abstract from purpose in the study of organs, tissues, and cells. In fact, the cellular theory is the most powerful fulcrum with which purpose has been and is still being rolled back from biology; thanks to this theory, mechanics, physics, and chemistry are applied to living organisms. The cellular theory applies to organisms in so far as they are mechanisms, but if one studies purposive organic behavior, one cannot start out from the cell and one cannot follow mechanistic methods. The cell, the concepts of structure and function, the causal principle, and objective time cannot be used as a framework for visualizing purpose-striving movements, since it leaves the time structure of these movements outside its scope. A mechanistic theory of man is neither complete nor scientific, because it does not take man's specific time structure into account and, moreover, such a theory does not explain the purposive behavior of some animals.

6. SUMMARY

Structure is the basis for function; no organic function exists without organic structure. Structure and function do exist without purpose, or life on the vegetative level without purpose-striving does exist. Structure and function are the substructure upon which purpose is built as a superstructure. Structure and function are omnipresent throughout the evolutionary scale, but in contradistinction purpose emerges gradually and becomes more and more crystallized as one ascends this scale. The concept of purpose applies with absolute certainty only to the human level of evolution. The fact that the cell is the building stone of all organisms without exception is clear evidence that structure and function are all-embracing biological principles. In the case of viruses, which do not have cellular structure, it is hard to say whether they are living organisms or extremely complex crystals. Allow me to clinch in an aphorism what has been said so far: *No life without cellular structure; no function without such structure; but there is life without purpose.*

CHAPTER THREE

NERVOUS SYSTEM AND MOVEMENT

All living organisms display mechanical movement. Some of them which possess nervous systems are capable of performing purposive movement. Therefore, one can ask two questions about the relation between nervous system and organic movement: (1) what is the relation between the nervous system and mechanical movement, and (2) what is the relation between the nervous system and purposive movement? The answer to the first question is clear-cut—this is a causal relationship and neurophysiologists are gradually unraveling its intricacies. But the second question raises utterly different problems because the time structure of purposive movement differs in essence from that of mechanical processes. Must biologists strive for monistic, mechanistic explanations of either type of organic movement, or should one acquiesce in dualistic theories of behavior?

First, I shall mention briefly the differences between mechanical and purposive movement; next, I shall compare a series of organic movements and then we shall try to decide which explanation is the most satisfactory all around, a monistic, causal, or a dualistic causal-teleological theory.

In the background looms the psychophysical problem, the unseen guest who spoils the dinner. No matter how one turns the problem of the relation between the nervous system and organic movement around, this stickler prevents the problem from coming to a standstill. It seems that there are only two ways out: either one ignores the psychophysical problem (monism), or, one throws up his hands and accepts it as an insoluble problem (dualism). I wish to defend the dualistic approach to living organisms, notwithstanding its defects. I do believe that the approach through the time problem enables one to state the psychophysical problem in a more satisfactory manner than has been the case heretofore.

I shall not follow this thought in any great detail because it would lead us too far afield.

I have consistently evaded the term "voluntary" movement so as to side-step the problem of "freedom of the will," or "freedom of choice." One can glean from a quotation from an article by Hughlings Jackson that biological definitions of volition are unsatisfactory. He defines voluntary activity simply by stating that it is not automatic reflex movement: "Most voluntary equals: least automatic!" He quotes Spencer in the same context, who expresses an identical thought: "Cessation of automatic action and the dawn of volition are one and the same thing."[1] Such definitions are circular; they should be replaced by more pertinent and more useful ones.

Purpose does not imply a purpose for which one strives consciously. The road is, therefore, open for developing this concept on different levels of consciousness; hence one can define freedom, or choice, in terms of such levels. I shall not follow this lead in what is to follow, because it is not necessary to define freedom, or choice, if one wants to define purpose. Purpose always points to a certain time structure, regardless whether one strives for a purpose in full consciousness.

The leading theme of this chapter is the defense of a dualistic theory of behavior in a negative sense, namely, that the relationship between nervous system and purposive movement cannot be of a causal nature. Physiological theories masquerade as causal explanations but upon further analysis one finds teleological contaminations tucked away in the structure and function of the nervous system; this structure and these functions are interpreted along teleological lines but biologists are, on the whole, not explicitly aware of this surreptitious teleology. If one accepts the dualism of mechanical and purposive organic behavior, one is forced to adopt the dualistic viewpoint, which postulates a causal relationship between nervous system and mechanical movement, but which leaves the relationship between nervous system and

[1] Hughlings Jackson, "Evolution and Dissolution of the Nervous System," *British Medical Journal*, 1 (1884), 591.

purposive movement in the dark. The entire argument will be conducted from the viewpoint of the time structure of organic movement.

1. MECHANICAL MOVEMENT AND PURPOSIVE MOVEMENT

Allow me to repeat what has been said before: the physical sciences describe movements of inanimate bodies, they break movement up in stretches with the aid of punctiform instants and geometric points, and these stretches are aligned in the before-and-after of objective time. These stretches of mechanical movement, separated from each other by point-instants, can be projected on a three-dimensional space co-ordinate system and a one-dimensional time co-ordinate. With these means one can measure movement and can express it in mathematical formulae. Movement of inanimate objects can be described with mechanistic methods because point and line can be applied to this modality of movement since it occurs in objective time.

Movement of living organisms which occurs in objective time, such as heart action, intestinal peristalsis, reflex phenomena, can be described by mechanistic methods. To study heart action, for instance, the physiologist makes a record of systole and diastole on a kymograph. The curve represents movement from one position in a point-instant (systole), through a stretch of space-time (venous blood filling the ventricles), to another position in a point-instant (diastole), and again, movement through a stretch of space-time (expulsion of blood from the ventricles) to another position in a point-instant (systole), and so on. The neurophysiologist who studies reflex action makes curves of the stimuli which he applies and of the motor response; he measures the time relationships between stimulus and response with appropriate clocks which write time markings on the record. Physiologists describe organic movement of the mechanical variety by the same methods that the physicist uses to describe movement of inanimate objects: space and time co-ordinates, clocks, and measuring rods, and they strive, whenever possible, to express their results in mathematical equations. This can be done because mechanical movement occurs in objective time. But one cannot treat purposive movements in this fashion, because they occur in subjective time.

The time structure of mechanical movement is that of a succession of stretches of movement, exterior to each other, separated by point-instants, but the time structure of purposive movement is that of the precious present,[2] where past, present, and future mutually interpenetrate each other. The precious present cannot be delimited by point-instants, it cannot be represented spatially by lines, since interpenetration cannot be so represented. Purposive movements project into the future and while they are, on the one hand, future-attuned, they emerge, on the other, from the individual's past—someone jumps over a high fence; in this jump, here-and-now, he actualizes movements which he has practiced over years and years, and so his past activities reverberate in his present act, which also penetrates into the future immediately ahead. His past and his future interpenetrate within the man's present and therefore his past and his future coexist with his present.

Because the time factor in purposive movement cannot be represented spatially, it follows that point, line, punctiform instant, time interval, measuring rule, clock, co-ordinate system, mathematics, and quantification are irrelevant in the study of these movements. Or again, that mechanistic methods are inappropriate for the study of teleological biological phenomena. One needs *teleological concepts,* one must develop the idea of *subjective time,* or the precious present, and one must follow an *introspective, anthropocentric approach* if one wants to get insight into purposive vital processes.

This plea for specific concepts, time-form, and approach in biology in the wider sense does not mean that this branch of biology must strip itself of the methods and the data of biology in the restricted sense; on the contrary, the real problem is how to integrate and dovetail both approaches. Let us consider a series of organic movements to support the dualistic viewpoint: the

[2] See Chapter Five.

knee tendon reflex, rhythmic activity of the respiratory center, erect stance, walking, reflex shutting of one eyelid, and conditioned reflex shutting of both eyelids.

2. MECHANICAL ORGANIC MOVEMENT

A. The Knee Tendon Reflex

A tap with a reflex hammer on the knee tendon suddenly lengthens the extensor muscles of the leg; this lengthening is the sensory stimulus. This stimulus is transmitted to the corpuscles of Pacini in muscles and tendons which "probably serve for the perception of movement . . . and pressure. . . ." [3] Electrical potential differentials are set up in the Pacinian bodies and these electrical impulses are picked up by the nerve endings which they enclose. The impulse is discharged along the sensory nerve toward the center where it enters into the posterior root ganglion. The steady state of the bipolar cells in this ganglion is disturbed and these cells discharge their impulses into the lumbar region of the spinal column where they take several paths: some of the inflow goes upward, some goes downward into the long fibers which connect the various segments of the spinal cord, and some of the inflow reaches the motor cells in the anterior horns of the lumbar spinal cord. The incoming stimulus fires the cells of the anterior horns into activity which is discharged into the outgoing motor nerves and so into the extensor muscles of the thigh. Through the motor end plates in the muscle the stimulus reaches the muscle fibers and causes contraction of these fibers and, therefore, the extensor muscles contract; the leg stretches slightly in response to the tap on the knee tendon. This superficial and sketchy description of a reflex mechanism is a thousandfold refined by the physiologist and the biochemist who find out new facts all the time. These details do not concern us here, because we are interested in the time structure of reflex phenomena compared with that of purposive processes.

Whether one studies reflexes in great detail, or whether one

[3] Stephen W. Ranson, *The Anatomy of the Nervous System* (8th ed.; Philadelphia: W. B. Saunders Co., 1947), p. 70.

takes an over-all view of these phenomena, *the time structure of reflexes is the before-and-after of objective time.* Before—tap on knee tendon; after—disturbance of steady state of Pacinian corpuscles; after—inflow of sensory stimulus; before—firing of motor neurones; after—outflow of stimulus through motor nerve; before —resting state of muscle; after—contraction of muscle fibers and movement of leg. The more detailed our knowledge about reflexes becomes, the more before-after sequences are added; an occurrence which covers a time interval of several tenths of seconds is cut up into a series of occurrences measured in milliseconds. Looking on from the outside, there is the enveloping, macroscopic before-after relationship: tap on knee tendon—movement of leg; the intermediate neural mechanisms fill in this larger interval in small stretches of time like a mosaic. But macroscopic and microscopic occurrences alike happen in the before-and-after of objective time.

Neuronal activities also happen in objective time: the activity of neurone "a" (before) causes neurone "b" to go into activity (after). And from the viewpoint of time it makes no difference whether neurones are aligned in a straight line, as in the simplest sensori-motor reflex arcs, or whether they function in a complicated feed-back network and relay system; the time structure of ongoing processes is that of objective time. The relationship between stimulus, neuronal mechanism and motor effect are clear-cut cause-effect relationships.

B. Spontaneous Activities of Neurones

When one cannot detect an outside stimulus nor any stimulus within the nervous system which is the cause of neuronal activities, one speaks of spontaneous activity; the electrical-action currents in the cerebral cortex which are recorded in the electroencephalogram are such spontaneous processes. How spontaneous are they actually? A good example of such activity is the rhythmic functioning of the respiratory center:

> The respiratory center is connected with, and controls the activity of, the lower neurones which supply the muscles of respiration. There is little doubt that the center possesses an inherent rhythmic-

ity, analogous to that of the sino-auricular node of the heart. Under experimental conditions it continues to discharge in a rhythmic manner after it has been cut off from afferent impulses from the lungs, the circulatory system, and higher centers, and after the respiratory muscles have been paralyzed by means of curare. The respiratory center of the goldfish continues to discharge rhythmically after the brainstem in which it is found has been excised.[4]

Physiologists record the rhythmic, "spontaneous" functioning of the respiratory center with appropriate apparatus. The spikes in this electrical record are synchronous with the rhythmic movements of the muscles of respiration; no doubt, the respiratory center causes contraction and relaxation of these muscles. This activity is non-reflex in nature, though the center is subject to influences from higher centers by reflex mechanisms: take a cold shower and you will notice that the cold stimulus over the skin of the back causes you to inhale deeply. But the rhythmic activity of the center is not reflexively induced and because we do not know of any reflex influences from higher levels which induce this activity, we call it a "spontaneous" activity.

This word is really a misnomer. Far from spontaneous, the functioning of the respiratory center is evidence of physicochemical processes going on within its neurones which are the cause of its rhythmic discharges. One has the causal chain: physicochemical processes in the neurones of the respiratory center—discharge of stimuli to the peripheral muscles—rhythmic contraction and relaxation of these muscles. One can give an account of what happens in the center, between center and periphery, and in the peripheral muscles on the basis of causality. True, even if these physicochemical processes were fully known, it would still be a mystery, most likely, why they are exteriorized as rhythmic stimuli. Now it is the fate of all science that causal chains are never fully known. No sooner is one question answered than a number of new questions arise because causal chains can be broken up again and again into yet smaller causal links, or the known chain can be connected with newly discovered collateral chains. However, no matter how complex causal relations are,

[4] Samson Wright, *Applied Physiology* (London: Oxford University Press, 1937), p. 442.

they always have the time structure of the before-and-after of objective time. To shift over from causality to teleology in the face of overwhelmingly complex causal relationships is uncalled for.

C. Erect Stance and Walking

When we stand erect we do not stand perfectly still, but our body sways ever so little now to the right then to the left, now forward then backward. This is a mechanical type of movement from a position in a point-instant to another position in a point-instant. The maintenance of erect posture depends on an intricate network of reflexes in which partake the vestibular apparatus, the cerebellum, the spinal cord, to name only a few of the structures which are involved in this mechanism. This is what happens: the body sways forward a little; this is a stimulus which disturbs the steady state of the otoliths, which stimulate neurones in the vestibular nuclei; by relays through the cerebellum, motor stimuli reach trunk and buttock muscles which pull the body backward slightly. The trunk goes through its center of gravity and leans backward a little, which position stimulates the vestibular apparatus once more into sending messages to muscles which cause the body to sway forward. And this goes on indefinitely. Neural mechanisms as well as swaying movements can be explained on the basis of cause-effect relations, since both processes occur in objective time. When we walk, the left arm balances the movement of the right arm; movements of arms balance movements of contralateral legs; forward thrust of right shoulder balances forward pull of left leg; the erector muscles of the trunk contract alternatingly; the entire complex mechanism of walking is initiated in the nervous system and it is causally related to the structure and function of the nervous system.

When one compares tendon reflex with activity of respiratory center, with erect stance, with walking, one will notice that more and more neurones become involved in this series of organic movements. And yet, all these movements are of the mechanical variety occurring in objective time. The greater complexity of the walking mechanism compared with the knee tendon reflex mechanism does not prove that walking is therefore a purposive movement. The fact that more neurones are involved does not lead to goal-striving attributes of these mechanisms.

3. PURPOSIVE ORGANIC MOVEMENT

Reflex Shutting of Eyelids and Conditioned Reflex Shutting of Eyelids

When a foreign body hits the cornea, a reflex mechanism is set in motion which causes shutting of the lid of the eye. But if a large, visible object comes flying toward one's face, one shuts the eyelids in anticipation of damage to the eyes; this is conditioned reflex shutting of the eyes, a reflex which does not exist from birth, whereas mechanical reflex closure appears to be inborn. Riesen has raised chimpanzee babies in darkness and he found that they did not react with defensive eyelid closure to large objects thrust toward the face, but that defensive movements in response to direct contact stimulus were present:

> Their reflex responses indicated that their eyes were sensitive to light—the pupils constricted; sudden changes of illumination startled the animals. . . . They did not blink at a threatening motion toward the face. When an object was advanced slowly toward the face, there was no reaction until the object actually touched the face, and then the animal gave a startled jump.[5]

After the animals had lived in a normally illuminated environment, conditioned reflex shutting of the eyelids was established after quite some time.

These two mechanisms, reflex closure and conditioned reflex shutting of the eyes, do not by any means involve the entire body; besides the *orbicularis oculi,* the neck muscles may contract—the animal or the person turns his head away from an oncoming large object; but on the whole, either manner of shutting the eye is limited to the same region of the body and the same segments of the nervous system and they involve therefore quite similar re-

[5] Austin H. Riesen, "Arrested Vision," *Scientific American,* 183 (July, 1950), 17.

flex pathways. And yet, reflex shutting and conditioned reflex
shutting of eyelids are phenomena of an entirely different nature
because there is an essential difference between the time structure
of these two types of organic movement: reflex shutting occurs
after the stimulus has impinged on the cornea; it is a sensori-
motor, cause-effect, before-after relationship in objective time.
But in the other case, the eyes are already shut *before* damage
can be done; these movements anticipate the stimulus. Now, anticipation of future events is foreign to the sensori-motor reflex
mechanism, as well as to any other cause-effect sequence—a cause-
effect relationship is not attuned to the future immediately
ahead. Conditioned reflex shutting of eyelids is evidence of foresight, of purpose-striving, of teleological organization, on account
of its being projected into the future. The word "purpose" is not
used in the sense of a purpose for which one strives consciously
and deliberately, but it points to the time structure of movement.
Long before we learn in detail what damage a large object may
do to our eyes, we have an awareness of impending danger, a
vague feeling of something out there, just about ready to thrust
itself upon us.

A sensori-motor reflex like the knee tendon reflex is clearly a
cause-effect sequence, but it is less obvious that spontaneous activity of the respiratory center is such a relation; in the former
instance the cause-effect relations are more easily visualized because one moves from the macroscopic level (tap on knee tendon)
to the physicochemical level (neuronal activities) back to the
macroscopic level (jerk of leg), while in the example of the respiratory center cause-effect relations remain shut up within the
neurones and on the physicochemical level. When we proceed to
erect stance and walking, yet another type of argument can be
raised against the causal interpretation of these movements—these
are movements of the entire body and they have quite another
meaning for us than the totally useless knee tendon reflex; it
seems difficult to accept the idea that stance and walking lie
within the realm of causality. There is little doubt that reflex
shutting of the eye on contact with a foreign body is a clear-cut
cause-effect sequence, though one usually assumes that this reflex

is purposive. Of course it isn't, the eyelids close only *after* the damage is done. But when we look at conditioned shutting of the eyes we have an entirely different order of events; this movement has a protensive, future-attuned nature, which is absent from the before-and-after time structure of reflex phenomena, rhythmic neuronal activities, erect stance and walking, reflex shutting of the eyelid. The time structure of conditioned reflexes must cause us to critically examine physiological theories of purposive behavior.

4. PHYSIOLOGICAL THEORIES OF BEHAVIOR

Physiological theories attempt to explain each and every organic movement from the same viewpoint, namely, that organic movement flows from the structure and function of the nervous system. One tries to prove that purposive as well as mechanical organic movements are causally related to the nervous system; i.e., one explains purposive movement on a mechanical basis. I shall bring out the teleological facets which are hidden in these so-called mechanistic, monistic theories, which are imbued with unrecognized teleological elements.

The confluence of four streams of thought generates physiological, mechanistic theories of behavior: (1) There is a gradual transition from mechanical movement to purposive behavior and there is no chasm between the two; (2) One believes that the spatial structure of the nervous system is teleologically organized, which is a remnant of Aristotelian teleology; (3) Identification with living organisms causes us to project psychological attributes onto neurones; (4) The sequence of sensory stimulus—motor effect—is more than a cause-effect sequence because it is teleologically interpreted; the organism is supposed to be lying in wait for the stimulus to impinge upon it.

A. The gradual transition from mechanical movement to purposive behavior

Biologists believe that there is a gradual transition from the straight-line, simple, sensori-motor reflex to the most complex reflexes which go through the highest cerebral levels. This belief

expresses the underlying premise that there is no essential difference between mechanical and purposive movement. According to
physiological theories, purposive movements are very complex
chain reflexes upon which an intricate network of feed-back relays is superimposed; intertwining sensori-motor reflex mechanisms on various levels of the nervous system co-operate to create
purposive movement. The only difference between mechanical
and purposive movement is, according to this point of view, that
there are more neurones involved in purposive behavior than in
reflex phenomena.

To show that this trend of thought is deeply ingrained not only
in physiology but also in philosophy, I quote Anatol Rapoport:

> It appears that our subjective experience of desire and intent is a
> crucial element in the genesis of a teleological explanation. Our
> projection of these subjective experiences on the outside world is
> at the root of teleological reasoning. The desire or intent is a sort of
> mental rehearsal of the act or of its result. Actually, the neural
> events associated with this anticipation of the result precede the
> act. But since we think of the result as being in the future, it seems
> to us that the "Future" (that is, the purpose) is the "cause" of our
> actions. . . . To us, the object we see is *"out there."* Similarly, the
> cause of our action seems to us to be "out there," in the future. But
> to someone able to observe our neural processes, our acts would ap-
> pear as simply the consequences of those processes. To him cause
> and effect would appear in their natural sequence. If moreover, he
> could *manipulate* our neural processes, he could fully predict our
> actions, and all traces of purposefulness would disappear (in the
> opinion of this superhuman observer) from our behavior. Purpose-
> fulness thus appears to be not necessarily something inherent in a
> situation, but rather something in the way the situation is evalu-
> ated.[6]

The kaleidoscopic picture of reflex activities seems to fit in
very well with these ideas. The two-or-three-neurone, one-level,
straight-line, sensori-motor reflex is relatively fixed and predictable; but the more a reflex is controlled by higher centers in the
brainstem, in the midbrain and, particularly, if it is under corti-
cal control, it becomes more and more variable, less and less pre-

[6] Anatol Rapoport, *Operational Philosophy* (New York: Harper & Brothers, 1954), p. 70.

dictable and seems gradually to assume the properties of purposive events. Reflexes on lower levels, normally under control from
above, are changed when this control is eliminated, as in hemiplegia; the tendon reflexes become exaggerated in the affected
limb because inhibition from higher centers no longer interferes
with and no longer tones down the inflow of sensory stimuli and
the outflow of motor impulses. In this condition one can observe
a remarkable inversion of the plantar reflex. Stimulation of the
sole of the foot causes plantar flexion of the big toe in a normal
adult person, but in hemiplegia and in other neurological conditions, this reflex is inverted to an extensor response of the big
toe, i.e., we find a positive Babinsky sign. This is the original
state of affairs; the Babinsky sign is positive in the newborn baby
whose pyramidal tracts are not yet myelinated and therefore not
yet capable of conducting inhibitory impulses from cerebral cortex to spinal centers. Superimposed upon the sensori-motor reflexes of the lower levels of the nervous system is the "internuncial
neurone network" which influences and modifies the processes
going on in the lower reflex arcs. The more internuncial neurones are interposed between sensory stimulus and motor response, the more variable and unpredictable is the reflex. Reflexes which involve the brain are relayed through the largest
possible number of internuncial neurones and they are therefore
the most complex and the least predictable of all reflexes.

It is most refreshing to hear how a mathematically oriented
neurophysiologist warns against these mechanistic trends. Householder warns that the complexities of the nervous system and the
truly stupendous numbers of neurones involved in neural processes must not cause us to forget that quantitative formulations
cannot account for purposive phenomena and least of all, for consciousness: ". . . It is neither to be expected nor to be desired that
quantitative formulations can in any sense represent all of the
complexities of any psychological process, or, a fortiori, the true
'inwardness' of conscious life." [7]

[7] Alton S. Householder and Herbert D. Landahl, *Mathematical Biophysics
of the Central Nervous System* (Bloomingdale, Ind.: The Principia Press,
1945), p. 115.

The argument that purposive movement is more complex than mechanical movement but that the two are essentially of the same nature does not hold; conditioned reflex shutting of the eyelids is a relatively simple purposive movement, while back and forward sway, which involves the entire body musculature, is a very complex mechanism indeed. Then there is the increasingly smooth performance of skilled movement with practice, which means from the physiological angle that fewer and fewer muscle fibers and neurones become involved and that these processes become, in a sense, simpler. A case in point are the graphs which Gesell has made of the behavior of young children—first they move about from toy to toy in a highly scattered and unpredictable pattern, but as they grow older, they move about less and less, they stay longer with the same objects, and their paths become much simpler.

On all counts, the difference between purposive movement and mechanical movement cannot be reduced to the degree of complexity of reflex mechanisms and to the number of neurones which are involved in these movements; purposive movement is not a complex version of mechanical movement, because there is an essential difference between the time structure of these two modalities of movement.

B. The Nervous System is Teleologically Structured

Physiological theories of purposive behavior claim that physicochemical processes, channeled by the labyrinthine structure of the nervous system, are exteriorized as purposive movement. This explanation flows from the intuitive conviction that all organic structure is intended for a purpose, which conviction becomes a strong belief when one looks at the nervous system. One insists that the structure of the nervous system is teleologically organized, and therefore one tries to explain both mechanical and purposive movement on the basis of the structure and function of the nervous system. Spatial schemata of the structure of the nervous system are the mainspring of explanations of all organic movement and as a consequence such theories overlook the specific time structure of purposive movement. We see purposiveness in organic structure; we hide purpose in structure, which is another way of saying that our thinking is space-dominated.

Scientists do not think any longer that atoms, that the solar system, are teleologically organized structures, yet we still think that the structure of living organisms is purposeful. One used to see purposiveness in the world of inanimate objects, but natural science learned some two, three hundred years ago to withdraw teleological principles from mechanics. Aristotle thought that everything that exists has its entelechy. Jaeger points out that this concept is misunderstood in biology, where entelechy has the meaning of an inner drive, specific for living beings.[8] Aristotle did not limit the concept of entelechy in this fashion, but he thought that everything, living or dead, was striving to get to its appropriate place in the cosmos. Galilei's experiments with falling bodies eliminated teleological thinking from mechanics and he brought the movements of inert objects strictly under the rule of the causal principle. Similarly, teleology has been rolled back considerably in biology since it was proved that respiration, heart action, reflex phenomena, stance, walking, co-ordination between groups of muscles, are cause-effect relationships. The mechanistic approach to living organisms has created the science of biology in the restricted sense. However, when one thinks that the purposiveness of organic movement is due to the structure of the nervous system, one unknowingly reverts back to the Aristotelian teleological conception of the organism. But Aristotle's interpretation of organisms was part and parcel of his general teleological conception of reality, whereas the teleology of biology in the wider sense is not a cosmic teleology at all; it is a severely restricted teleology based on the analysis of the time structure of purposive movement.

C. The Projection of Psychological Attributes on Neurones

Compare a living organism, now moving this way, then that, with the swaying branches of a tree, with the movements of a cloud, with Brownian movements of particles which can be seen

[8] Werner Jaeger, *Aristotle, Fundamentals of the History of his Development* (Oxford: Clarendon Press, 1948), p. 384.

under the microscope, and the impression is forced upon us that
the behavior of living organisms and movement of inanimate objects are essentially different types of movement. We think that
an ameba which puts out its pseudopods, an ant which is pushing
and pulling a piece of material, a dog jumping up at his master,
are purposive processes, and that the swaying of the tree, the
movements of a cloud and of microscopic particles are mechanical movements. But let us be clear about it, this impression
which holds on to us with the force of an obsessive idea does not
stem from scientific observation, but from a prescientific approach
toward and observation of reality. This prescientific attitude may
be justified in observing the dog's behavior, but we must carefully scrutinize this attitude when we study the behavior of ants
or amebae. It is the attitude of identification with living organisms. This identification leads us to project some of our own psychological attributes upon organs and upon cells. It seems as if
cells possess human attributes of intellect, choice, freedom, purposive movement. We are apt to see a spark of intelligence and of
purpose-striving in the movements of an ameba who puts out its
pseudopods and envelops its prey. A clear-cut example of such projection of psychological attributes on the cell can be found in
Monakow's and Mourgue's work: "The living cell with its reaction
of klisis and ekklisis, its rudiment of discriminatory activity or
protodiakrisis, which function is exercised entirely independently
from any rigorous tropism which can be reduced to exact determinism of a physico-chemical nature. . . ." [9] Pavlov has tried to
establish a mechanistic, physiological theory of purposive behavior on the basis of the doctrine of conditioned reflexes. He
speaks of "analyzers" and "synthesizers" which are supposed to be
localized in different regions of the cerebral cortex and which
are supposed to explain conditioned reflexes.[10] Pavlov means to
erect a mechanistic theory of behavior and he wants to eliminate

[9] C. von Monakow and R. Mourgue, *Introduction biologique à l'étude de
la neurologie et de la psychopathologie* (Paris: F. Alcan, 1928), p. 11.

[10] Ivan P. Pavlov, *Conditioned Reflexes* (London: Oxford University Press,
1927), p. 110.

psychology from the field of science, but in postulating the presence of analyzers and synthesizers, he projects psychological attributes upon certain brain cells; his mechanistic theory is shot through with teleological contaminations; this is the result of our unrecognized tendency to identify ourselves with living organisms, their organs, and their cells. One identifies oneself with neurones, one projects psychological attributes on them, and therefore one thinks that cells are more than physicochemical action centers. Sherrington warns against such projection of mental attributes on neurones in these words: "The cell-organization of the brain may be the key to the secret of its correlation with mind but not, it would seem, by individual mental endowment of its constituent cells." [11]

We are so spellbound by the mystery of life that we intuitively identify ourselves with all that lives and this identification is the primary reason why we conceive all living organisms as purpose-striving beings. We bring prescientific ideas about life with us into the biological laboratory, into the psychiatric office, to the psychological scoreboard, to the patient's bedside; these ideas do not fit into the mechanistic conception of living organisms toward which biology in the restricted sense is building.

D. The Teleological Interpretation of the Stimulus-Response Sequence

The concept of stimulus-response is one of the fundamental concepts of biology. Basically, this is a cause-effect relation, except that certain teleological afterthoughts make it into a hybrid, causal-teleological concept. The neurones on the sensory end of a reflex arc seem to be lying in wait, as it were, for the stimulus to impinge upon them; the organism seems to be in readiness to receive the stimulus. This "attitude" of the organism adds a protensive, future-attuned quality to the physicochemical processes which take place at the periphery of a reflex arc. Such anticipatory qualities are absent from a pure cause-effect sequence. The

[11] Sir Charles Sherrington, *Man on his Nature* (The Gifford Lectures, 1937-1938; New York: The Macmillan Company, 1941), p. 269.

water in the oceans does not keep itself in readiness to respond with flood to the attraction of the moon; it is simply a before-after relationship in objective time without teleological attributes.

The teleological interpretation of the stimulus-response sequence runs parallel to the idea that neurones have vaguely delineated psychological attributes; one thought reinforces the other. Over and above these interpretations of neuronal activities there is the teleological interpretation of the structure of the nervous system; if one thinks that the structure of the nervous system is purposive, then it follows that stimulus-response sequences which take place in the nervous system are purposive. Thus the entire gamut of thoughts, 1, 2, 3, and 4, conspire to derive purposive movements and their time structure from the spatial structure of the nervous system and its functioning in objective time. Inevitably, the characteristic time structure of purposive movement is lost sight of.

5. RELATION BETWEEN NERVOUS SYSTEM AND PURPOSIVE MOVEMENT

Two classes of biological phenomena meet in the central nervous system of man and of higher animals: events that belong to the world of causality and events that belong to the teleological order. Many an attempt has been made to describe and explain the meeting and interlocking of these two aspects of some living organisms. Descartes thought that every time mind influences body through the pineal gland a miracle takes place; he conceived of a kind of *deus supra machina;* an act of God interlocks with mind-body relations and rescues man's innate freedom of the will from rigid determinism of the body machine. Physiological theories really are not so very different; they project psychological attributes on neurones and they postulate a *deus in machina,* or, at any rate, a *homunculus in machina.* This artifact gets around the fact that neural mechanisms lack protensive, future-striving properties, and it serves to explain why these properties are present in purposive movements. According to the physiologists, one progresses from less complex movement and neural mechanisms to more complex movements and neural mechanisms when one ascends from knee tendon reflex, to abdominal reflex, to controlled emptying of bladder and rectum, to stance and walking and dancing, and finally, to highly skilled finger movements and speech. Since there is a gradual transition from one movement to the other and from one governing neural mechanism to the other in this ascent, there is between them only a difference in the degree of their complexity. All these movements are initiated by the nervous system, all of them occur in objective time, and the entire spectrum of organic movement can be overarched by the causal principle. A similar transition from less complex to more complex movements and neural processes which exist in each individual can be observed as one ascends in the evolutionary scale; the structure and function of the nervous system become increasingly complex and this lesser or greater complexity explains why some lower animals are capable only of simple sensori-motor reflexes, while mammals and man with their highly complex nervous systems are also capable of performing purposive movements and highly skilled finger movements. Thus, one tries to build a monistic, natural scientific theory which explains all organic movement based on the causal principle.

This trend of thinking has been reinforced by the performances of modern machines regulated by feed-back mechanisms. These cybernetic machines are supposed to be more or less faithful models of purposive behavior of higher animals and man. Since regulation by feed-back mechanism is undoubtedly one of the mechanical functions of the nervous system, cybernetics plays right into the confused causal-teleological thinking in neurophysiology. Rosenbluth, though pleading for the elevation of purpose to the status of a scientific concept, nevertheless overlooks the essential differences between mechanical and purposive behavior:

> . . . a uniform behavioristic analysis is applicable to both machines and living organisms, regardless of the complexity of the behavior. . . . The methods of study of the two groups are at present similar.

Whether they should always be the same depends on whether or not there are one or more qualitatively distinct, unique characteristics present in one group and absent in the other. Such qualitative differences have not appeared so far.[12]

It seems to me that such qualitative differences are there for everyone to see, namely, the difference between the time structure of mechanical movement and of purposive movement.

In order to settle the problem whether or not machine models can represent purposive behavior, one must bring some deeply hidden obscurities in biological thinking out into the open; on the one hand, one adopts the common-sense, prescientific view that all organic movement is essentially different from movement of inanimate bodies, and, on the other, one thinks that there is a gradual transition from mechanical reflex movement to purposive movement. To confuse matters further, this smooth transition is ruffled by injecting teleological elements into mechanistic explanations; one projects psychological attributes onto neurones and teleological properties onto the structure of the nervous system.

Mechanistic theories of organic behavior start out from the premise that all organic movement occurs in objective time. But if one accepts that there is an essential difference between the time structure of mechanical and of purposive movement, one must conclude that dualistic theories are indicated. These theories come up against the intrinsic difficulty how to relate the structure and function of the nervous system to purposive movement. *Neural mechanisms occurring in objective time cannot explain purposive movements which occur in subjective time.* Can one go beyond this negative statement and can dualism explain what relationship does exist between the nervous system and purposive behavior?

Physiologists will flaunt in the face of this negative conclusion the results of some experiments and evidence from neurological diseases which seem to prove that purposeful movement is caused by neural mechanisms; given a well defined lesion, one can pre-

[12] A. Rosenbluth, N. Wiener, and J. Bigelow, "Behavior, Purpose and Teleology," *Philosophy of Science,* 10 (1943), 22.

dict that a fairly well defined change in the behavior of the patient or the experimental animal will be the result. Carpenter's experiments with monkeys are a case in point; he made minute lesions in the basal ganglia of monkeys with the Horseley-Clarke apparatus; these lesions caused hemiplegia of one arm and leg, and a few weeks after operation a tremor of the Parkinsonian type appeared in the affected arm.[13] No doubt, the lesion is the cause of the hemiplegia and of the tremor, or, the other way around, the hemiplegia and the tremor can be localized in the lesion. But what do these experiments prove in relation to purposive, normal behavior of the intact monkey? Do they prove that purposive movement can also be localized in the nervous system, or that the nervous system is the cause of purposive movement? Both hemiplegia and tremor are instances of mechanical non-purposive movement which can be treated with the quantitative methods of natural science, with the use of ingenious devices which fit the neurologic situation. Carpenter made points of reference on the arm of the monkey and on the cage in which the animal was kept, he made a cinematographic record of the movements of the animal and he analyzed the record quantitatively:

> Measurements of the movement-amplitude were made by the method of point-deviation (measurement of the distance of a reference point on the moving member from a static reference point in the environment of the animal). Projected point-deviation measurements in millimeters were projected to actual point-deviation in millimeters by proportional scales, and the figures were plotted with actual point-deviation as the ordinate and time in frames as the abscissa.[14]

These mechanical, non-purposive movements are causally related to the abnormal function of the damaged basal ganglia, but these facts by no means prove that purposive movement is causally related to the intact nervous system and its normal functioning. In the first case there is a causal relationship between neural

---

[13] Malcolm B. Carpenter, John R. Whitter, and Fred Mettler, "Tremor in the Rhesus Monkey Produced by Diencephalic Lesions and Studied by Graphic Method," *The Journal of Comparative Neurology,* 93 (1950), 1-15.
[14] *Ibid.*

mechanisms inside the nervous system and mechanical movement observed from the outside; in the second case we are looking for a relationship between inside neural mechanisms in objective time and outside purposive behavior in subjective time. The nature of the relationship between neural mechanism and purposive behavior is shrouded in darkness on account of the difference between the time structure of these two sets of processes.

The limb afflicted by the Parkinsonian tremor goes from one position in a point-instant to another position in a point-instant in objective time; neural mechanisms occur in objective time also; point-instants apply to both the inside mechanism and the outside, gross movement. But purposive movement cannot be broken up in stretches by point-instants since it occurs in subjective time; there cannot be a causal relationship between neural mechanism in objective time and purposive behavior in subjective time, since causal explanations are valid only within the context of objective time.

Laboratory experiments and neurological cases do not answer the question how neural mechanisms are related to purposive movement. All that experiments and pathology prove is that *man and some animals are capable of performing purposive movements on the condition that the structure and function of the nervous system are intact, but these normal conditions are not the cause of purposive movements.* Breakdown of the structure of the nervous system is followed by the disappearance of some purposive movement, e.g., the monkeys in Carpenter's experiments cannot peel a banana very well with their hemiplegic hand, and at the same time so-called "involuntary" movements appear in the form of a Parkinsonian tremor. But from this negative finding, the disappearance of purposive movement, one cannot conclude that there exists a causal relation between normal structure and function of the nervous system and normal goal-striving behavior.

Causal relationships exist between neural mechanisms and movements, like stance, complex reflexes, spontaneous activities of nerve centers; occurrences within the organism and in its environment form a long and involved network of interrelated causes and effects which, together, make it possible that the organism continues to exist in objective time. If there is a break somewhere in the causal chain, either inside or outside the organism, all these marvelous mechanisms and movements are gradually, or suddenly, no longer possible and the organism either becomes sick, or it dies. One need not invoke teleology to explain the breakdown of normal mechanical vital phenomena; wherever there is a break in a causal chain, whether in a living organism or in the world of inanimate objects, the entire system either changes or breaks down.

This negative conclusion shows up the unsatisfactory state of our insight into psychophysical relationships. All one can say is that the intact structure and function of the nervous system are the condition without which there can be no normal psychophysical unity, but the structure and function of the nervous system do not give a causal explanation of this unity.

6. MONISM AND DUALISM

One can sum up the monistic, mechanistic, physiological theory of purposive behavior in three statements:

1. All organic movement is purposive, including movements of the ameba and straight line, sensori-motor reflexes; there is an inkling of purposive-striving even in these almost mechanical movements.

2. All organic movement is causally related to the structure and function of the nervous system; the function of the nervous system consists of physicochemical occurrences channeled by its structure.

3. All organic movement lies within the realm of causality.

Tersely stated in this fashion, one can clearly see that the monistic viewpoint becomes involved in contradictions because conclusion (3) is the exact opposite of statement (1). This contradiction flows from our not recognizing the essential difference between mechanical and purposive movement and from tucking teleology away in the cell and in the nervous system. One creates a surreptitious teleology interlarded with causality in assuming

that ameboid movements are more than physicochemical processes, or again, that sensori-motor reflexes show purposive tendencies. The labyrinth of causal interrelations in the world of inanimate objects does not press the physicist or the chemist into
thinking beyond causality; why then should the biologist in the
restricted sense hide his limited causal knowledge behind "spontaneous activities of neurones," "analyzers and synthesizers," "the
organism-as-a-whole"? These concepts are vague and ill-defined,
since one mixes teleology into explanations which can very well
be carried by the causal principle. The approach, the methods,
and the time form of biology in the restricted sense are all of one
color, since our thinking remains within the causal realm. The
cell is a physicochemical action center without attributes of choice
or intelligence. Sensori-motor reflexes are cause-effect sequences
without foresight or purpose-striving. The nervous system is the
meeting place of physicochemical forces which are channeled by
reflex arcs, internuncial neurone networks, feed-back relays, so
that there is a marvelous co-ordination between various organic
functions. No matter how complex, these relations are causally
determined. But the purposiveness of some organic movements
cannot be explained on this basis. Here one needs a different
approach.

The monistic conception of behavior has its shortcomings because it can in no way explain the obvious differences which exist
between man and animals. Man makes tools, he writes and speaks,
he creates works of art and buries his beloved ones after death.
If one insists that the entire field of human and of animal
behavior is homogeneous and that the structure and function of
the nervous system do explain organic behavior in all its aspects,
then one has to shut his eyes to the abyss between man and animals. Physiological theories of behavior overlook these differences
because they start out from the premise that there is a gradual
transition from mechanical reflex to purposive movement. If the
biologist says that the existence of art, religion, ethics is none of
his business, but the philosopher's or the divinity student's, he is
quite correct if he is a *pur-sang* biologist in the restricted sense.

But the biologist in the wider sense is sooner or later inexorably confronted with questions that fall outside the scope of natural science. The strength of biology in the restricted sense lies in its natural scientific, objective approach, its quantitative aim; because its objects occur in objective time, it is akin to the mechanistic natural sciences. Its weakness shows up when one looks at vital phenomena in their entirety; the physicist, the astronomer, the chemist, study a homogeneous sector of reality; for instance, the irregular distribution of matter in space is only a quantitative heterogeneity which the astrophysicists study with mechanistic methods. Living organisms, on the contrary, are an essentially heterogeneous field of study, since purposive movements differ in essence from mechanical movements, and how shall one explain these essentially different movements with identical principles?

The dualistic theory of organic movement can be clinched in the following statements:

1. Most movements of all organisms are of the mechanical variety; they exist in objective time, they are within the realm of causality; the same mechanistic methods which one uses to study movement of inanimate objects, namely, co-ordinate system, clock and measuring rod, apply to this class of organic movement; the ultimate goal is to measure mechanical vital phenomena. Some movements of some organisms are purposive, their time structure is past, present and future interpenetrating each other (subjective time); they are within the teleological realm; they cannot be studied with mechanistic methods and they cannot be measured.

2. Mechanical organic movements are causally related to the structure and function of the nervous system; the relation between nervous system and purposive movement, however, is an enigma.

3. Dualism of approach, of concepts and of time forms is indicated in biology because mechanical movement belongs in the context of objective time, causality, and the extraspective approach; purposive movement belongs in the context of subjective time, teleology, and the introspective approach.

The material of biology is essentially heterogeneous, hence there is no alternative but to build dualistic theories of behavior of man and of higher animals. The teleological aspects of behavior cannot be anchored upon structure and function, they cannot be studied with mechanistic methods and they go beyond the causal principle. The concept most needed in the study of purposive behavior is subjective time. Specific biological teleological concepts must be integrated with a specific approach toward purposive behavior. Biology in the wider sense must start out "from above," with man, unlike biology in the restricted sense which starts out "from below," with the cell (Kurt Goldstein).[15] This anthropocentric approach from above seeks to understand, first, our own purposeful movements, then those of our fellow men, and finally the purposeful movements of some higher mammals, by empathizing with the synthesis of past, present, and future in subjective time which these movements accomplish. The approach from above evades the pitfalls of mechanistic physiological theories of purposive behavior because it refrains from projecting psychological properties upon neurones and from attributing teleology to the structure and function of the nervous system; one does not try to express the time structure of purposive movement in spatial schemata. The approach from above is one way to stop the confusion between the concepts of structure and function and the concept of purpose. Finally, the approach from above opens up the possibility of defining causal unity versus teleological whole. If one restricts teleology to the context of subjective time, and if one uses causality in the context of objective time, one clarifies basic biological concepts, though this dichotomy by no means sheds light on the relationship between nervous system and purposive movement.

Physiological theories of purposive behavior are dominated and supported by spatial schemata; however, spatial schemata of the structure of the nervous system cannot clinch the time structure of purposive movement, because subjective time defies spatial representation. Biology in the wider sense is a time-dominated

15 Kurt Goldstein, *Der Aufbau des Organismus* (The Hague: Nyhoff, 1934), p. 1.

science. I am tempted to say that one becomes obsessed by the idea of subjective time in order to roll back space-dominated thinking and Aristotelian teleology of spatial structure. This requires constant effort. For instance, one compares the neck of a bird with the human neck; and the conclusion forces itself upon us that the smooth transition from the bird's pointed head to its torpedo-like body is purposeful because it facilitates flight; this spatial structure diminishes resistance while the bird is passing through air. On the other hand, one can conceive the shape of the bird's neck, its rigid spinal column, the placement of the feathers in the wing, etc., just as well from a causal viewpoint; the structure of the bird represents a number of causal links in a complex causal network which makes flight possible. All one describes is how objects interact in space and in objective time; the scientist should stop wondering whether these spatial arrangements are purposeful. The spatial configuration of living organisms is no evidence of the purposiveness of structure. Purpose is an actuality only in those movements of man and of certain animals which occur in subjective time. To speak of the purposiveness of organic structure is expressing purpose in terms of spatial relations, which means, hiding purpose in the structure of the nervous system or in the cell. Purpose must be beckoned out of its hiding place. One must develop an ear for the manner in which purposive movements occur in time in order to roll back space-dominated thinking.

CHAPTER FOUR

EMBRYOLOGY

So far we have discussed movements of adult organisms which are more or less stationary as far as their internal organic structure is concerned. The movements of an animal stalking his prey, of a man making a tool, are the expression of a relationship between the organism and the outside world. But the structural changes which take place in the hatching egg, in the developing embryo, are almost entirely restricted to the growing organism itself, separate from the outside world. These structural changes are a distinct class of vital phenomena which differ considerably from mechanical organ functions and from purposive movements. The problem arises whether embryological development can be described and explained by mechanistic methods, or whether it is teleologically constituted. Whether to stick to causality or to think in teleological terms is the dilemma in which embryology is caught up and it is this alternative that is behind the traditional controversy: mechanism versus vitalism. Although the hot war between these two factions has cooled off considerably in the past twenty-five years, the basic issues which are involved in this controversy have by no means been resolved and the problem continues to harass those biologists who are interested in basic concepts and fundamental methods.

Briefly stated, this is the problem: Is the progression from fertilized egg to fully grown organism a causally determined process, or is it of a teleological nature? I shall try to show that the hidden problem is this: Is the *structure* of the egg, of the embryo, of a teleological nature? And are the movements taking place in development purposeful movements? The answer to these problems lies in looking at development from the viewpoint of time.

I shall use as examples of embryological development only the very first and relatively simple stages. Beyond these, a brief description is quite impossible, as one would get lost in a maze of details without doing justice to the facts.

Development begins when egg and spermatozoon come together. The spermatozoon is chiefly a nucleus propelled by a long flagellum; the egg cell consists of a nucleus floating in a large amount of reserve food substances. Under the microscope the egg looks like a tiny, transparent vesicle with a thin membrane in which one can hardly detect any structure. There are the nucleus and protoplasmic granules, that's all. Sir S. H. Hardy, as he is quoted by Needham, describes it thus:

> Let us consider the egg as a physical system. Its potentialities are prodigious and one's first impulse is to expect that such vast potentialities would find expression in complexities of structure. But what do we find? The substance is clouded with particles, but these can be centrifuged away, leaving it optically structureless, but still capable of development. . . . How shall sources and sinks of energy be maintained in a fluid composed of eighty percent of water? They are undoubtedly there, for the egg is a going concern, taking in oxygen and maintaining itself by expenditure of energy.[1]

The very first step in development is that the spermatozoon penetrates the membrane of the egg cell; after penetrating it promptly loses its tail. A fertilization membrane forms around the egg which prevents penetration by a second sperm cell.

Now things happen in rapid succession. The nucleus of the egg and of the sperm cell partake of complicated mitotic divisions, the reduction division, which results in the exchange of their chromosomes and the expulsion of the two polar corpuscles. After the reduction divisions are completed, the combined number of chromosomes of egg and sperm is reduced to one half of the combined total, so that each cell of the future embryo will possess the number of chromosomes which is specific for a particular species.

After the reduction divisions are completed embryonal development proper starts. The first line of cleavage divides the fertilized

[1] Joseph Needham, *Chemical Embryology* (New York: Cambridge University Press, 1931), p. 612.

egg in two blastomeres. The first line of cleavage determines the future midline of the embryo and therefore each blastomere is destined to develop into one half of the adult individual. In the next few hours more lines of cleavage appear, each perpendicular to the previous one, and so the two blastomeres grow into a clump of cells, the morula. First we have two, then four, eight, sixteen and finally thirty-two blastomeres.

The next major step is the formation of a tiny cavity in the center of the morula; this stage is called the blastula.

Now an interesting and amazing event occurs: the blastula invaginates at one of its poles and so forms the gastrula. In this stage there are two surfaces of the young embryo: an outer surface which is directed toward the outer world or the ambient fluid, or surrounding cells, and an inner surface which lines the primitive body cavity. The gastrula is the simplest model of any adult organism: a tube with an inner and an outer surface. As development goes on, the structure of this tube becomes more and more involved and the steps which lead to these complicated structures are so intricate that they defy schematic presentation. Let us therefore break our description off at the stage of the gastrula. These early stages exemplify the general principles of embryological development and this is sufficient for our purpose.

When one thinks about these general principles and methods one encounters the same questions which have harassed us in the previous chapters, namely: Is the structure of the egg of a teleological nature, or should one conceive this particular organic structure as a physicochemical action center, in the same way as one would regard the structure of adult organisms? We shall see that embryologists teeter back and forth between these two ways of looking at organic structure.

Embryology describes how a fertilized egg develops into a full-grown organism. In order to describe this progression, one breaks the unitary, uninterrupted process up into partial processes, delimited by artificially designated stages. Early development is broken up in the blastomere stage, the morula, the blastula, and the gastrula stages. One describes each partial step, lifted out of the process in its entirety.

This "atomization" of natural phenomena is not limited to embryology, it is one of the generally accepted and essential methods of natural science. All embryologists break development up in stages, but besides this common denominator there are marked differences—some embryologists emphasize the structural approach, others favor the functional approach.

Some are mostly interested in the changes in structure that lead from one stage to the next, while others want to go beyond a purely descriptive embryology; they study the forces which cause one stage to develop into the next. The differences between these two approaches are more fundamental than the terms, descriptive-static and functional-causal-dynamic, would indicate. Those interested in structure for its own sake are more prone to allow teleological interpretations to creep into their descriptions, while those embryologists who study the causes which link one stage to the next attempt to eliminate whatever teleology still lingers on in their thinking.

Embryology has remained a purely descriptive science longer than most of the other departments of biology. Needham points this up as follows:

> That there is at present a certain gulf between the physico-chemical research and the "form" and the "shape" of the morphologists is a fact which must be faced. In present-day biology there lives on, still very hale and hearty, the essence of the distinction made by Aristotle between ὕλη and εἶδος, matter and form. It is probably at bottom this which inspires statements so often made by morphologists that do what one will with chemical methods, the meaning of form in animals will always elude one's grasp, for it belongs to another order of existence, a range of concepts intrinsically remote from physics. In so far as the form of living organisms is an expression of a degree of organization higher than anything with which the sciences of the nonliving world have to deal, it is true that we have to deal with something very different from mere heaps of molecules, but crystal form and the colloidal state, which exhibit an intermediate degree of organization, exist in the inorganic world and can be dealt with by the quantitative methods of physics and chemistry.[2]

[2] *Ibid.*, p. 554.

In other words, the morphologists interpret organic structure as belonging to the realm of the purposeful which is a world quite distinct from the realm of causality. Although Needham helps to clarify the distinction between the structuralists and the functionalists in embryology, he nevertheless intimates that there is a gradual transition between the structure of inorganic matter and organic structure, in the sense of a greater complexity of the latter. Neither the structural nor the functional approaches in embryology try to define the differences and the relations between causality and teleology, and therefore the structuralists and the functionalists talk mostly past each other.

The mechanistic embryologist is a causalist, he is less interested in structure and its changes, since he is devoted to the task of uncovering the links between individual stages; he sticks closer to the atomization of the developmental process. The vitalist is a teleologist who is haunted by the idea of the εἶδος, of purpose-determined form, and he conceives the process in its entirety in sort of an artistic bird's eye view. He thinks less about the connections between individual stages and more about such a problem as how the individual is contained, *in potentia,* in the egg cell, and about the over-all, sweeping progression from egg to adult organism.

The concept of potentiality is not limited to biology, it is also an important concept in the sciences which deal with inanimate objects. But here it has an entirely different connotation than in embryology, as one can see from the following examples. The atom contains, *in potentia,* a tremendous amount of energy, an amount which was long ago predicted by Einstein's formula, $E = mc^2$, in which "E" stands for the amount of energy contained within the atom, "m" for its mass and "c" for the velocity of light. Hydrogen and oxygen, given certain conditions, have the potentiality to form water. In order to run a hydroelectric power plant one collects water in a mountain reservoir where it represents a large amount of potential energy; the water is directed downward through huge tubes and it makes dynamos rotate which generate electricity. All these events, except in so far as man intervenes and channels them, are purely causally determined processes and no physicist or chemist would dream of invoking teleology in order to explain them. In the natural sciences the concept of potentiality fits into causal explanations.

But the statement that the egg contains the adult organism *in potentia* has teleological overtones. Driesch postulates that the egg has an entelechy, a principle which somehow steers the physical processes going on in development. The entelechy, or, "that which carries its own goal within itself," is supposed to explain why the potentiality of the egg is transformed into an actuality. Needham takes issue with this conception and tries to look at the potentiality of the egg in the same way as the physicist looks at the potential energy contained within an inanimate system:

> Chemical embryology . . . will affirm that if we knew all there is to be known about the physico-chemical constitution of the egg, we should be able to predict the results of its development. . . . we do expect some day to be in a position to offer a reasonable causal explanation of the origin of all the measurable properties of adult living beings and from the measurable properties of their eggs, and form is evidently one of them, just as physical constitution.[3]

Needham urges the use of mechanistic, natural scientific methods in embryology to their fullest extent, as firmly as Claude Bernard was convinced that these methods should be applied in physiology:

> . . . To say that the development of a living being can best be described in a metrical or mechanical way is not to say that it *is* metrical or mechanical and nothing else. The physico-chemical embryologist is not committed to any opinion on what his material really is, but he is committed to the opinion that the scientific method is one way of describing it and that it is best to apply that method in its full vigour if it is to be applied at all.[4]

The mechanistic approach makes continuous headway in embryology. Recently, Burr has developed a technique for measuring small electrical potential differentials in developing chick and salamander embryos. He comes to the conclusion that the electric field which exists already in the stage of the fertilized egg is one

[3] *Ibid.,* p. 558.
[4] *Ibid.,* p. 17.

of the mechanical factors which play a determining role in development:

> This means that with this new technique it is possible to measure with certainty and accuracy at least one of the organizing agents of living things. . . . Therefore, we have another bit of evidence which indicates that these electrical fields are not mere by-products of metabolic activity, but in all probability are irreducible organizers of the pattern of living organisms.[5]

Teleological interpretations reverberate in the writings of most biologists, *sotto voce* in those of the mechanists and quite openly in some statements by vitalists. As an example I quote Rignano:

> The direction of the ontogenetic development toward a predetermined end is also influenced by the fact that the embryo overcomes early disturbances which might deflect it from its course. Ontogenesis seems to be marshaled by some occult intelligence or entelechy in the same way that the construction of a machine and the direction of its work is presided over by the mind of the engineer.[6]

Sinnott expresses teleological thoughts in a much more restrained and tentative fashion, merely suggesting that development is more than a purely mechanical process:

> This unfolding pattern toward which development proceeds is evident in normal embryology, though here it is so familiar that we often forget how amazing it really is. To watch an animal egg cleaving in a precise fashion and marching inexorably toward its culmination in the adult, or to see a bud unfolding into an intricate system of leaf and flower, particularly if these progressions are observed when speeded up by time-lapse photography, gives us a vivid impression of activity which is goal-directed. Whatever we may think of it in theory, the organism *looks* as if it were going somewhere.[7]

Driesch believed that he had settled the dispute between mechanists and vitalists on the basis of some ingenious and fundamental experiments, which are still of great value, though few

[5] H. S. Burr and C. I. Hovland, "Bio-electric Potential Gradients in the Chick," *The Yale Journal of Biology and Medicine*, 9 (1936-37), 257.

[6] Quoted in Needham, *op. cit.*, p. 17.

[7] Edmund W. Sinnott, "Biology and Teleology," *BIOS*, 25:1 (March, 1954), 38.

biologists nowadays share Driesch's teleological interpretation. He divided the fertilized eggs of sea urchins after the first line of cleavage was completed, i.e., in the stage of two blastomeres. Each blastomere is floating in sea water separate from its partner. An amazing thing happens—a complete though small individual is formed by each blastomere. In other words, each blastomere has the potentiality to form an entire organism, but under normal conditions this full potentiality is not actualized, it is kept in check. What influence, what force is it that keeps each blastomere in check when they develop as partners, one into the right half, the other into the left half of the embryo? Vitalists like Driesch and Rignano claim that it must be a meta-causal or teleological principle which sees to the suppression of the potentialities of the blastomeres.

Why is it that embryologists are likely to go beyond causal explanations into the realm of teleological interpretations while physiology has narrowed its base line down more and more to causality? Embryology is still a stronghold of teleological thinking because of the singular nature of its subject matter. Development is an irreversible, unidirectional, noncircular, and nonoscillatory process. Once fully grown, the organism maintains itself by reversible, circular, and oscillatory processes. Organs function in a full-grown organism in the sense of a pendulum movement. Heart action is the classical and most lucid example; it moves back and forth between systole and diastole (systole $\rightleftarrows$ diastole). Functioning neurones move incessantly back and forth between the steady state and the excitatory state (steady state $\rightleftarrows$ excitatory state). These processes are causally determined changes of the spatial structure of cells and organs, occurring in objective time. Organ functions are nondirectional processes, since they are circular or oscillatory processes. This is not the case in embryology. Development goes relentlessly ahead without pause nor retreat, it does not oscillate back and forth like a pendulum movement.

The question that harasses both mechanists and vitalists is this: Where does this direction come from? Some postulate a meta-causal entity as entelechy, but such hypotheses have a mystical quality and they do not fit into the mechanistic approach which is taking over from pure description. But this reluctance to go beyond causality does not mean that one eliminates teleology. One is convinced that development is more than a causally determined process, and therefore teleological ideas, however vaguely formulated, continue to have a strong influence in embryological circles. One thinks, on the one hand, that as yet little known physical, chemical, electrical forces are the causes why the blastula invaginates at one of its poles and so forms the gastrula. But over and above this causal explanation one assumes that the progression from one stage to the next has a time-synthesizing aspect. One assumes that the blastula synthesizes the blastomere stage which has just been completed with the gastrula stage which is just now appearing. One thinks that development occurs in subjective time. Bowman says:

> The life-process as a whole, therefore, is presupposed in each of its successive phases. Each moment in the process is at once an epitome of what has been and an anticipation of what is to be. The time of the living being is so far like the time of experience—spirit-time,—rather than the time of physics.—Life, therefore, transforms the time of physics into another kind of time: and the time of life, like the time of experience is characterized by the distinction of past, present and future.[8]

I would object that the distinction between past, present, and future can be observed and studied, without a doubt, only in our own purposive movements. These movements are surely time-binding processes, but there is no proof that the embryo is a time-binding entity.

We are the victims of appearances. We think that we observe our own time structure in the developing embryo. We ourselves strive relentlessly forward in time, developing, maturing, aging, and finally dying. In each of these phases of human life something of our past reverberates, and each phase is a preparation for what is to come. We read the time structure of our goal-directed acts

---

[8] Archibald Allan Bowman, *A Sacramental Universe, Being a Study in the Metaphysics of Experience* (The Vanuxem Lectures, 1934; Princeton: Princeton University Press, 1939), p. 363.

into the unidirectional developmental processes going on in the embryo. Crudely speaking, we think that the egg and the embryo are homunculi. The first people to look through a microscope in the seventeenth century, with the exception of Leeuwenhoek, said that they could see a little man sitting hunched up in the sperm cell. We smile at such flights of fancy, and yet, we believe that we have a great deal in common with the embryo, since we do think that the time structure of the developmental process is similar to our own time structure. In other words, we identify ourselves with the embryo.

It is easier to overlook this identification with one's subject matter in embryology than in physiology, because the time structure of development sets this process apart from mechanical organ functions. Teleology is strong in embryological theories because one is not aware of his identification with the embryo, and this leaves the door open to smuggle in all manner of concepts which do not belong. The vitalistic embryologist projects human psychological attributes onto the egg and onto embryonal cells under various guises of "entelechy," "hormè," "élan vital," or an occult intelligence. We have encountered similar artifacts in the previous chapter where we have seen that one projects psychological attributes onto neurones. Identification and projection are much to blame for the confusion between causality and teleology. This confusion about general principles is due, in part, to our not sensing the difference between the time structure of embryological development and of our goal-striving movements; in part because the concept of purpose is an ill-defined and poorly delineated concept in biology; and it is in part due to our not being aware of our attitude of identification with the embryo.

The mechanistic embryologist thinks that teleology is as unnecessary in his field as it is in physiology. He predicts that developmental mechanics, physics, and chemistry will eventually furnish complete causal explanations, as far as scientific explanations can ever be complete; and one will not feel the need any longer to fall back on teleological interpretations. It is already possible to explain Driesch's experiments on sea urchin eggs on a causal basis. Many hormone-like substances have been isolated from various parts of embryos, which substances have a directive influence on the structural changes which are going on. Each blastomere secretes hormone-like substances which keep its neighboring partner in check, but when they are separated from each other, these substances do not find a point of attack and therefore there is no restricting influence on each half-egg, which goes on to form a whole embryo. Under normal conditions, these hormone-like substances are one of the causes that the right blastomere forms the right half, the left blastomere forms the left half of the embryo. The invasion of mechanics, physics, and chemistry in embryology rolls teleology back from one of its traditional strongholds.

If one wants to go beyond a causal explanation of development, one might heed the following points: (1) We believe that the spatial structure of the embryo is teleologically constituted, which means that one buries purpose in structure; (2) the directedness which is such an outstanding feature of development is taken as evidence that embryological development is a goal-striving process; however, irreversibility is not sufficient proof that an event is of a purposive nature; for instance, the increase of the entropy of the physical universe is such a directed, irreversible process; (3) one assumes that each stage of development sums up the previous stages and that it projects itself into the next stage, i.e., one assumes that embryonal development occurs in subjective time; (4) these hypotheses and assumptions flow from the attitude of identification with the embryo and this identification leads to projecting human attributes of foresight and goal-striving onto the egg and onto the embryo, which is an anthropomorphic way of looking at development.

We can get a clearer insight into these problems if we take note of our innate drive to identify ourselves with all that lives. This insight is promoted also if we define the concept of purpose in biology as clear-cut and as strictly as possible. I propose that we limit the use of the concept of purpose to events which occur in subjective time, events which synthesize past and future in the present. We have evidence that our own purposive movements accomplish such a synthesis; we have good reason to believe that the purposive movements of some animals are capable of such a synthesis in time, in a mitigated manner; but we have no evidence that the egg or that the embryo accomplishes such a synthesis. This precise and narrow definition of purpose leaves development outside the realm of the purposive.

To many this may seem an unsatisfactory conclusion. One would expect that contemplating the methods of embryology would clarify the basic biological concepts of structure, function, and purpose because of its extraordinary subject matter. The evidence both from the theoretical and from the practical side shows that development is a causally determined process occurring in objective time. These processes do not give a fresh slant on the concept of purpose and, therefore, embryology does not help to differentiate structure and function from purpose. The definition of purpose in terms of events which synthesize the past and the future in the present may be incomplete. There may be other meanings of the word purpose which have not been touched upon and which may be relevant in embryology. But one need not define the concept of purpose as completely as possible if one sets the limited goal of separating structure and function from purpose. Embryology does not help in reaching this goal.

The embryologist describes the changes of the spatial configuration of the growing embryo in space and in objective time. Now that embryology is becoming more and more imbued with the methods of mechanics, physics, and chemistry, it is no longer an exclusively descriptive science. Instead of describing each structural state and resting our case there, we analyze how one phase of development causes the occurrence of the next phase. Embryology is becoming a dynamic science which looks at development from the functional point of view. In this respect, embryology is closely akin to physiology.

This kinship is fundamental. It flows from the time structure of physiological functions and the time structure of embryological development—both occur in objective time. Embryology studies causal relations between spatial structures which are changing in objective time.

Let me summarize: Embryological development occurs in objective time. Embryology does not analyze phenomena which occur in subjective time. It does not deal with purposive phenomena. Its general concepts are: structure, function, causality, and objective time. Embryology does not help to define the concept of purpose nor to differentiate structure and function from purpose.

CHAPTER FIVE

OBJECTIVE TIME AND SUBJECTIVE TIME

The dual time schema of objective time and subjective time is impressed upon us from two directions: from the side of reality where there are nonpurposive phenomena in objective time and purposive phenomena in subjective time, and from the side of the observer who must approach nonpurposive, vegetative vital phenomena with an extraspective attitude and with objective methods, but who must study purposive vital phenomena with an introspective, empathic attitude and from an anthropocentric viewpoint. Object, time form, and method of study are mutually related.

Inherent schisms exist in reality which cannot be explained away. The physical sciences attempt to create a unitary conception of a world existing in space and in objective time, but biology must build up a dualistic theory because it is confronted with opposites such as: living organisms versus inanimate objects; man versus woman, adult versus child; normal mentation versus abnormal mentation; man versus animals; living on the vegetative level and on the purposive level; structure and function versus purpose; causality versus teleology. It would be foolhardy to try to explain all these disjunctions as flowing from the concepts of objective time and subjective time; nevertheless, all of them are at least related to the basic differences between these two time forms. The contrasts—structure and function versus purpose, life on the vegetative level versus living on the purposive level, biology in the restricted sense and biology in the wider sense—can be anchored upon inherent differences between objective time and subjective time.

1. OBJECTIVE TIME

Synonyms: physical time, clock time, calendar time, measurable time, time expressed in terms of space, *temps espace* (Bergson).

Definition: objective time is time expressed in terms of space, it consists of (a) intervals and (b) punctiform instants, which delimit an interval.[1]

St. Augustine describes the punctiform instant as follows:

> How much so ever if flown away, is past, whatsoever remains, is to come. If any instant of time be conceived, which cannot be divided either into none, or at most into the smallest particles of movement, that is the only it which may be called present; which little yet flies with such full speed from the future to the past as that it is not lengthened out with the very least stay. For lengthened out if it be, then is it divided into the past and the future. As for the present, it takes not up any space.[2]

Bergson has shown extensively how we use the punctiform instant to measure time; the punctiform instant is the chief means whereby we express time in terms of space:

> We shall take note of the exact instant when a movement begins, that is to say, the simultaneity of an external change and one of our psychological states; we shall take note of the moment in which the movement stops, that is to say, yet another simultaneity, finally we shall measure the space traversed which is in fact the only thing that can be measured. Therefore, there is no question here of duration but only of space and of simultaneous events.[3]

Interval of objective time and punctiform instant are correlated and mutually determining concepts. The interval starts and stops abruptly in two punctiform instants which encompass it.

---

[1] Adrian C. Moulyn, "The Functions of Point and Line in Time Measuring Operations," *Philosophy of Science*, 19:2 (April, 1952), 151-152.

[2] St. Augustine, *Confessions*, trans. William Watts (New York: G. P. Putnam's Sons, 1931), Bk. XI, ch. 15, p. 243.

[3] Henri Bergson, *Essai sur les données immédiates de la conscience* (53rd ed.; Paris: Presses Universitaires de France, 1946), p. 86.

The interval of objective time has homogeneous duration and therefore it can be represented by uniform movements of celestial bodies and of clocks. The punctiform instant is devoid of all and any duration and, consequently, it can be represented by a geometric point. This representation is possible because all spatial elements have been removed from the geometric point. A point-instant is a punctiform instant represented by a geometric point; one abstracts from time and space in creating the concept of point-instant.

The punctiform instant is the cornerstone concept of time-measuring because it cuts up the "streaming of time" into intervals which can be represented by stretches on a line. Time comes to a standstill in punctiform instants, even as the movements of clocks are periodically brought to a standstill by the escapement mechanism. The astronomer interrupts the movement of the earth artificially and in his imagination when the vertical line which he erects in the place of observation goes through the azimuth. Objective time is measured by uniform, interrupted motion of clocks or of other objects which move uniformly from one position in a point-instant to another position in a point-instant; the length of the straight line which lies between two point-instants is the standard for the time interval to be measured. The standard unit for time-measuring is the rotation of the earth around its axis, i.e., from point-instant midnight to point-instant midnight. The unit for time-measuring is the length of the circle traversed by the point of observation, namely, the circumference of the earth. This circle is cut up in subdivisions by a multitude of points so that one subdivides the period from midnight to midnight into the smaller units of time-measuring; the solar day is cut up into hours, hours into minutes, and so on.

I want to make it clear that circular reasoning lies hidden here; objective time is measured by means of uniform mechanical movement, but, the other way around, mechanical movement occurs in objective time by definition. We use objective time to define mechanical movement and we use mechanical movement to measure time and to define objective time. I see no way out of this circle; however, one can place it parallel to another circle.

The relation between subjective time and purposive movement is also bilateral, or circular; one can define purposive movement on the basis of its occurring in subjective time and one can define subjective time by pointing to the properties of purposive movement. Circular definitions are distressing to the logical mind, which wants to develop one concept out of the other; but there may be solace in pointing out that wherever one is dealing with general, basic concepts, a logical derivation in a straight line is quite impossible. Take, for instance, the concept of inanimate matter; one can go no further in defining this concept than to fall back on exactly what the prefix "in" implies, namely, that it is not living matter and thus one is forced back to the problem how to define living matter. Many scientists have acknowledged that this is an impossible undertaking. But if one acquiesces in the parallel opposites of mechanical movement versus purposive movement, and objective time versus subjective time, then one can stop the confusion between the concepts of purpose, structure, and function, and one need no longer see purposiveness in organic structure and function.

2. SUBJECTIVE TIME

Synonyms: psychological time, mental time, time which cannot be represented spatially, *temps durée* (Bergson), time which cannot be measured, the precious present.[4]

Definition: Subjective time consists of a past fringe, a present with duration, and a future fringe.

I want to deviate from traditional nomenclature in introducing the term "Precious Present," in contradistinction to Clay's and James' term: "Specious Present." We are looking for a term which covers the moment of subjective time in which we perform purposive movements, in which we act or decide, and to call this moment a "specious present" indicates that one is not convinced that such a moment actually exists as a reality. Webster's dictionary defines the adjective "specious" as follows: "Superficially attractive, but not so in reality; deceptively beautiful. Specious

---

[4] A. C. Moulyn, *op. cit.*, p. 150.

implies a fair appearance with intent to deceive." [5] Clay, who introduced the term, believes it to be an illusion:

> The present to which the datum refers is really a part of the past—a recent past—delusively given as being a time that intervenes between the past and the future. Let it be named the specious present and let the past be known as the obvious past. All the notes of a bar of a song seem to the listener to be contained in the present. All changes of place of a meteor seem to the beholder to be contained in the present. At the instant of the termination of such a series no part of the time measured by them seems to be a past. Time then, considered relative to human apprehension, consists of four parts, viz., the obvious past, the specious present, the real present, and the future. Omitting the specious present, it consists of three . . . nonentities: the past, which does not exist, the future, which does not exist, and their conterminus, the present; the specious present is a fiction of experience.[6]

William James has elaborated on Clay's concept of the specious present as follows, giving the impression that, deep down, he does not believe in its speciousness:

> In short, the practically cognized present is no knife-edge but a saddleback, with a certain breadth of its own on which we sit perched and from which we look in two directions of time. The unit of composition of our perception of time is a *duration*, with a bow and a stern as it were—rearward- and a forward-looking end. It is only as parts of this *duration block* that the relation of succession of one end to the other is perceived. We do not first feel one end and then feel the other after it, and from the perception of the succession after an interval of time between, but we seem to feel the interval of time as a whole, with its two ends embedded in it.[7]

> The specious present has, in addition, a vaguely vanishing backward and forward fringe, but its nucleus is probably the dozen seconds or less that have just elapsed.[8]

[5] *Webster's New International Dictionary.*

[6] E. R. Clay, *The Alternative* (London: Macmillan & Co., 1882), Bk. I, ch. 14, par. 104, p. 167.

[7] William James, *The Principles of Psychology* (New York: Henry Holt & Co., 1931), I, 609-610.

[8] *Ibid.*, I, 613.

James's entire argument is based on sensory perception in artificial, experimental settings, not on human acts as they unfold in subjective time. This is probably the reason why he overlooks the most baffling of all problems: how do we live and act and move into the future which lies immediately ahead? This oversight of the importance of the future in the fringe is all the more apparent since it is tucked away in a footnote: "Again I omit the future, merely for simplicity's sake." [9] But this is an oversimplification, since the whole, perplexing problem of human time structure revolves around the question how we live into the future which lies immediately ahead.

Further elaborations on the idea of the specious present are hardly helpful in getting the central problem into focus, which is, how we human beings live in time. Alexander mentions our future tendency but bases his statements on sensory experience, not on the act:

> Thus the specious present is not present at all but includes within it distinctions of past and present. We may add future as well. For the broad present may contain at least dawning ideas of what is to come, and even dawning sensory objects, for in vision anyhow we have corresponding with after-sensations, 'before-sensations' in the process during which a color sensation is gradually rising to its full intensity or saturation.[10]

Volkelt rather talks around the concept of a precious present, saying: "The now is impressed upon us as coming from the before and as streaming into yet another now; there is, so to say, no room for this in a point without duration." [11] "In the certainty of the now is given for me the certainty of the future simultaneously with certainty of the past." [12]

Bergson has brought new ideas to the time problem; he differ-

[9] *Ibid.*, I, 641.

[10] S. Alexander, *Space, Time and Deity* (The Gifford Lectures, 1916-1918; New York: The Humanities Press, 1950), I, 122.

[11] Johannes Volkelt, *Phänomenologie und Metaphysik der Zeit* (Munich: C. H. Beck, 1925), p. 30.

[12] *Ibid.*, p. 24.

entiates *"temps espace"* from *"temps durée."* *"Temps espace,"* or time expressed in terms of space, consists of intervals, exterior to each other and succeeding each other; it is the time of astronomy, physics, of biology in the restricted sense, and of daily routine living. *"Temps durée"* is the time of our inner life as it actually occurs within us, a time which cannot be expressed by means of the symbolism of spatial forms.

> Pure duration cannot be anything else but a succession of qualita-
> tive changes which melt into each other, which penetrate each
> other, without distinct outlines, without any tendency to exteriorize
> some in relation to the others, without any relationship to number:
> this would be pure heterogeneity. . . . as soon as one attributes the
> slightest degree of homogeneity to duration, one introduces space
> surreptitiously.[13]

Existentialist philosophers, and Heidegger in particular, have studied the time problem exhaustively. John Wild has given a concise synopsis of this point of view, showing that much of existentialist thinking about time is in harmony with Bergson's analyses. Wild differentiates between two modes of time, world time and human time:

> Everything in the world of nature seems to be engulfed in an
> irreversible flux of time which cannot be quickened or retarded but
> flows everywhere at a constant rate.[14]

> Physically, man is restricted to a momentary present, with a brief
> tendential background and foreground. But cognitively he may
> wander without restriction through all the ranges of time. . . . un-
> like the processes of nature, he is not divided from his own past
> and future. He can hold all the parts of himself together all at once,
> thus attaining an integrity of thought and action which is closed to
> any type of process or event.—In the full integrity of his existence,
> he is more than a process in time. [That is, in world time.] [15]

Permit me to describe the precious present, or subjective time, or human time, as I see it. The precious present consists of a past

[13] H. Bergson, *op. cit.*, p. 77.
[14] John Wild, "The New Empiricism and Human Time," *The Review of Metaphysics,* 7:4 (June, 1945), 543.
[15] *Ibid.*, pp. 555, 556.

fringe, a present instant with duration, and a future fringe. I
have borrowed the word "fringe" from William James, since it
indicates quite vividly that the subjective past and the subjective
future infiltrate diffusely in opposite directions away from the
actual present. An important aspect of the two fringes is that they
are asymmetric: the past fringe may be short, or relatively long, or
very long, depending on the age of the individual and on the act
which he is here-and-now performing. The past fringe may recede
into years and years past, or again, it may cover only the very
recent past of the last few minutes. In contrast, the future fringe
never projects ahead very far. The future fringe is short and if it
is at all possible to refer its duration to objective time, it lasts
usually several seconds and at most something like a few minutes
into the future. The fringes of the precious present cannot be
measured in seconds, minutes or hours, because they cannot
be delimited by punctiform instants. Subjective time cannot be
atomized by point-instants.

The precious present has duration. Since we are preoccupied
with time-measuring in our daily lives and in science, we think of
the present in terms of the punctiform instant and therefore it is
difficult to grasp the idea of a present which has duration. The
duration of the precious present differs from the duration of a
time interval because objective time is an homogeneous continuum, while the present instant in which we act and decide is
heterogeneous and discontinuous. The actual present interpenetrates with its two fringes; therefore, one can hardly say when the
past fringe ends and when the present is upon us, nor when the
present stops and when the future fringe begins. In thinking
about subjective time we must familiarize ourselves with the idea
of interpenetration in time and we must drop the idea that one
can determine, knife-sharp, when and where past, present, and
future begin and end. Intervals of objective time are juxtaposed
in a before-and-after relationship in succession; they are separated
by punctiform instants, but the two fringes are not separated from
the actual present by punctiform instants. Geometric point and
straight line do not fit into the world of subjective time, hence

the precious present cannot be expressed in spatial schemata and it cannot be measured. The subjective past and the subjective future blend into the actual present as an interpenetrating threesome, each influencing the other. The punctiform instant and the interval of objective time link our attention away from the inherent vagueness of subjective time and onto the discrete and symmetrical spatial schemata of objective time. In order to develop the concept of the precious present, we must switch over from space-dominated thinking to time-dominated thinking. Spatial schemata do not help in this readjustment: to the contrary, they hinder our thinking about subjective time.

3. THE DERIVATION OF OBJECTIVE TIME FROM SUBJECTIVE TIME

Objective time is subjective time expressed in terms of space. In order to express subjective time by means of spatial schemata, a complicated and in many ways contradictory process of abstraction takes place. An interval of objective time is derived from subjective time by the homogenization of the heterogeneous duration of a precious present. The punctiform instant is derived from the precious present by abstracting from time entirely. These processes of abstraction make it possible to represent the homogeneous duration of an interval by uniform motion and to represent the punctiform instant by the interruption of such a motion. The uniform, circular movement of the hands of a clock indicates "straight" lines which represent time intervals. I have pointed out elsewhere [16] that the concept of the straight line is represented not only by spatial elements, but that it contains a time element as well. A straight line is the shortest distance between two points not only in space but also in time. This dual character of the straight line injects time elements into time-measuring which detract from the clear-cut definition that objective time equals time expressed in terms of space. However, from a practical point of view, this definition serves a purpose. In time-measuring we think

[16] A. C. Moulyn, *op. cit.*, p. 144.

of the spatial relations between the hands and face of the clock; all other means of time-measuring rest on the spatial representation of time.

The punctiform instant is symbolized by the escapement mechanism of clocks, because this mechanism brings uniform motion periodically to a standstill. The astronomer brings the celestial clock periodically to a standstill in a punctiform instant by dint of his imagination and without relying on machinery to the extent that we do in daily life. The punctiform instant is an even more problematical concept than the time interval. One has to think of it as not encompassing any time whatsoever. Our early training in geometry is of some help, since we were asked to think of a geometric point which has no spatial dimension whatsoever. And since we are constantly using clocks, first in social life, in order to keep appointments, and later in science, in order to determine the simultaneity of events in a much more precise fashion, we readily gloss over the enigma of the punctiform instant; it is an enigma because the punctiform instant is not time at all. Its only use lies in time-measuring. In short, time-measuring is a complex procedure which uses both intellectual and mechanical means to express time in terms of spatial schemata, and this procedure rests on the concepts of the straight line and the geometric point.

Let me sketch the intellectual process of abstraction which shapes the precious present into objective time. An interval of objective time is fashioned from a precious present by removing the fringes. The present instant with duration is now no longer flanked on either side by a vague fringe but it is staked off by two punctiform instants. The simplification of the precious present goes further; its heterogeneous duration, which has elements of past, present, and future interpenetrating each other, is homogenized and we imagine that it is a "present" interval. But the only rationale behind this abstract way of dealing with time is that now the time interval is representable in terms of a straight line by the intermediary of the uniform motion of clocks.

The derivation of objective time from subjective time counteracts our tendency to think of these two modalities of time as running parallel to each other. We are likely to think about time in this fashion because we are constantly busy with time-measuring. And to measure time we always place two mechanical movements parallel to each other; the measuring movement and the movement to be measured. For instance, train conductors use the tiny movements of their watches to measure the large movement of the train. We must watch out that we do not fall prey to an analogy: we must not think that as the watch runs parallel to the train, so does objective time run parallel to subjective time. The precious present is the primary time mode from which one deduces objective time by a process of abstraction. The punctiform instant is a precious present totally detemporalized and represented by the interruption of motion which is brought to a standstill in a geometric point. And what happens to the fringes in this process of abstraction and transformation? Paradoxically, the fringes are magnified to unlimited dimensions; they become the past eternal and the future eternal. The objective, eternal past and the objective, eternal future are essentially symmetric, since both have unlimited dimensions. Yet, one has the feeling that the future eternal must be shorter than the past eternal because the past is growing all the time, while the future is infringed upon by the present, moving into the future and making it past. This discrepancy between mathematics and common sense becomes understandable if one accepts that the concepts of eternal past and future are derived from subjective time; the small dimension of the future fringe of a precious present and the relatively much larger dimension of the past fringe cause us to think that the objective future, too, must be shorter than the objective past. This is one of the numerous examples of our thoughts about subjective time influencing our ideas about objective time. The entire problem of time comes closer to its solution if we think that subjective time is the primary time form, while objective time is derived from it by a process of intellectual abstraction and the practical manipulation of movement.

In comparing objective time with subjective time one will find that the words "past," "present," and "future" have quite different meanings within the contexts of these two time forms. The past, present, and future of objective time are public, measurable time expressed in calendars and with clocks; future and past are symmetrical, since both are infinite. Both the objective future and the objective past are a homogeneous continuum; today, like yesterday, like tomorrow, will contain the same number of hours; from one to two P.M. equals from four to five P.M. Past, present, and future of subjective time are private, nonmeasurable, they are not *the* past, present, and future, but *my, your, their, our* past, present, and future. Past and future of subjective time are asymmetrical; the future fringe is short, the future of objective time is unlimited, or as long as you wish to conceive it; subjective time is a heterogeneous discontinuum.

Objective time and subjective time constantly interact and mutually influence each other, so that it is difficult to fixate the concept of subjective time. My future, five years from now, is a combination of objective calendar time, say September of 1961, infused with and superimposed by the future in the fringe of my private, actual present in which I am here-and-now in September of 1956 thinking about that future date. I think myself into this future date as if it were an actual present with a future fringe and hence, my thinking about the objective future "September 1961" becomes polarized by the future in the fringe of the precious present in which I am now living.

The objective future and the future in the fringe have a quite different structure. The future in the fringe is continuous with the actual present; the objective future may be a fraction of a second, hours, years, or eons ahead of the punctiform instant from which the objective future is figured. The future in the fringe is short, while the objective future may be extremely short or extremely long. The future in the fringe cannot be delimited by two punctiform instants in the way that the objective future is delimited; therefore the objective future is determinate and measurable. Tomorrow starts in the punctiform instant midnight and it ends in the punctiform instant midnight twenty-four hours later; periods of a year, a century, are staked off by punctiform instants also. The actual present in which we experience the coming of the new year cannot be delimited by two punctiform instants; this experience is, therefore, strangely mysterious, as the discrepancies between objective time and subjective time edge in upon our consciousness.

The objective past and the past fringe show similar differences, except that the past fringe may be relatively long compared to the future fringe; in some of our acts we revive memory images which have been stored for years or decades. Since memories of different vintage go into the act, the past fringe has a diffuse, irregular structure, while the objective past is continuous and homogeneous. The objective past is encompassed by two punctiform instants, while the past fringe begins irregularly and vaguely in the remote and recent, private past, and it partakes of the actual present with which it mingles and interpenetrates. Therefore neither fringe can be staked off by punctiform instants. When we place ourselves back into our own or into other people's pasts, we imagine that this past precious present is an actual present again and instead of static, dead past, it becomes the really living past once more. It is the historian's job to recreate the past as if it were again the actual, really living present.[17] Or, as Sheldon expresses it: "We don't merely contemplate the past as by intellect, we feel it, and incipiently act it. We are back there, not physically of course, but mentally. Time is indeed reversed in the living mind in such cases and by the affective-conative experience." [18]

We live always into the future in the fringe whether we are active here-and-now, whether we are planning for a future period, or whether we are remembering or conjuring up past occurrences. Man cannot extricate himself from subjective time which always influences objective time.

The determining characteristic of objective time is juxtaposition, while interpenetration is typical for subjective time. Interpenetration is impossible in objective time, since one time interval does not overlap with another interval; they are either contemporaneous or they are separated by a punctiform instant;

[17] Heinrich Rickert, *Die Grenzen der Naturwissenschaftlichen Begriffs-bildung* (Tübingen: Mohr, 1921), pp. 437-438.

[18] Wilmon H. Sheldon, *God and Polarity* (New Haven: Yale University Press, 1954), p. 596.

the interval nine to ten o'clock is external and juxtaposed to the interval ten to eleven o'clock, separated by the punctiform instant ten o'clock. Interpenetration is expressed in the concept of the precious present, whose past fringe and future fringe interpenetrate within the actual present with duration. In order to understand the structure of subjective time we have to liberate our thinking from domination by spatial schemata and from objective time which is expressed in such schemata. The punctiform instant cannot be applied to subjective time, hence this time form cannot be expressed in terms of space.

Besides juxtaposition and interpenetration there is another, equally basic difference between the two time forms. Objective time is continuous, subjective time is discontinuous. This aspect of time is particularly hard to grasp. We cannot think of any "holes" cut out of space, of discontinuous space-without-space, any more than we can think, initially, of empty, discontinuous time. But daily experience teaches us that our living in subjective time is actually discontinuous. We cannot remember and we cannot know from first-hand experience what goes on while we are asleep, except for the few seconds or minutes that we dream. Although we experience discontinuity in the waking-sleeping cycle, we deny the discontinuity of experience in subjective time, by filling in the gaps in our own experience with information that others give us and by relying on clocks and calendars. Besides sleep there are many other instances of discontinuous experience, like waxing and waning of attention, and lapses of consciousness when utterly fatigued. We are deathly afraid to admit that our life in subjective time is actually discontinuous; we shy away from the ephemeral, perishable precious present. If we do accept discontinuity of our very existence, what then do we do in these periods? The discontinuity of subjective time upsets our neat schedules of objective time to which we have harnessed ourselves. To nullify the discontinuity of subjective time we emphasize objective time and we believe that time must be continuous, although our experience belies our theories. The theory of the continuity of time is fathered by an ill-meaning sponsor—fear of death. It takes courage to uphold in the face of this fear that subjective time is actually discontinuous and that life on the purposive level is discontinuous.

Our thinking about subjective time is beset with many difficulties. We are used to *going with* the stream of objective time, it takes effort to *lift ourselves out of* this stream; we are forever occupied with measuring time; we cannot detect a specific organ for the perception of time.

A specific attitude is needed to gain insight into the time problem. In thinking about events in objective time one goes with the stream of time, but to describe our experience in subjective time one must lift oneself, so to speak, out of the stream of time in order to look simultaneously at the present, ahead into the future, and back into the past. Subjective time is not unidirectional like clock time, but, if you will permit me the expression, it is triple-directional. One must relinquish the schema of objective time which goes from past to future and which erases the present as an actuality. Instead, we must ensconce ourselves in a precious present to grasp past, present, and future as an interpenetrating threesome. To gain this insight, it is imperative to give up all ideas of time measurement.

It is often stated that the time problem is so mysterious because we do not have an organ with which we perceive time. We assume rather uncritically that we do have an organ for space perception, which is the inner ear, consisting of semicircular canals, ampullae and otoliths. However, this is an overstatement of the facts because these organs react to movements of our body and we do not really perceive space with them. We are capable neither of space perception nor of time perception, but we do perceive movements of our body in time and in space with various sense organs among which the inner ear plays a leading role. Although we do not have an organ for time perception, we can extrapolate spatial and temporal elements from sensory experience, because the importance of these elements varies from one sense organ to another. In the visual sphere the spatial aspect of experience is more important, while temporal elements dominate the auditory sphere. The eye is largely an organ of orientation in space, while the ear is, to a much greater extent than the eye, an organ of time integration. The ear is one of the bridges which lead us into the world in time because those auditory impressions which are most important to us, that is the spoken word, occur in succession in time. One might say somewhat loosely that there exists an antagonism between the ear and the eye—the eye takes in the world as it exists statically in space, while the ear takes in the world as it exists dynamically in time. All sensory modalities, including the ear, give us information about our location in space and about our living in time, but time shapes and determines the world of sound. For these reasons we shall gain insight into the time structure of mental processes more readily by analyzing the world of sound than by analyzing the visual world.

Since it is my good fortune that I can speak from experience both as a listener to and as a performer of music, I want to digress into this field for a moment. Musical experience is a complex process of time integration. While composing and playing music and while listening to it, we integrate objective time with subjective time. Let us first look at the subjective side of this process. We can point up in music, more convincingly than in any other realm of human endeavor, interpenetration in time, and particularly projection into the future fringe of a precious present. A brief and superficial analysis of a melody shows clearly the reality of the precious present. We hear a melody now, we still hear backward in time the part of the melody that just now has fallen silent, and we are expecting the oncoming phrase of the melody. Present, past, and future are so minutely attuned to each other in music that it taxes the imagination.

Let us look at the first six notes of our national anthem. As soon as we hear "Oh say," we expect that "can you see" will follow. Some measure of expectation is experienced, even if we had never heard this melody before. The sequence of the first three notes is a downward falling melodic line reinforced by an angular, broken rhythm. These properties of the first phrase prepare us for the second phrase. The three notes of "can you see" display a smooth rhythm and the melodic line strives upward. During the second phrase we look backward at the falling line and the broken rhythm of the first phrase. Anticipation and tension, generated by the first phrase, are relieved by the second phrase because the melodic lines and the rhythms are in contrast to each other. We feel all the more gratified since the melody comes momentarily to a standstill in a long, high note on the tonic. These two phrases bring about rise and fall of mental tension by virtue of their opposite musical properties and because these six notes intermingle and interpenetrate in subjective time.

Looking forward to "can you see" and looking backward over "Oh say," happens in four to five seconds of clock time. This process of time integration is not an analytical, conscious, intellectual act. We can describe this act only on the analytic, intellectual level but such a description is not accurate, it is only tentative and indicative. To bring to the fore that there is a vast difference between the description of time integration in musical experience and this experience itself, consider that it takes several minutes to read the foregoing analysis of the first six notes of the national anthem and that it takes only four to five seconds to sing these notes.

An expectant attitude, or projection into the future in the fringe of a precious present, is one of the outstanding characteristics of musical experience. Before we start to sing, we take a breath, i.e., we think about the song before the singing starts. The performing professional musician is fully conscious of the fact that he projects the music into the future immediately ahead.

The beginning of Beethoven's *Fifth Symphony* is a most mysterious instance of tension toward the future in the fringe. This tremendous work begins with an eighth rest: with silence. Nevertheless, the professional musician and the initiated amateur feel the tension of this silent moment, just before the great down-beating motif itself begins.

We steadily look ahead into the fringe of a precious present while listening to the development of a melody; we constantly look backward in the immediately preceding past fringe at the phrase of the melody we have just heard, and we are aware in the actual here-and-now that the melody is emerging from the past fringe and projecting into the future fringe. The composer, the performer, and the listener interlace present with past with future in a precious present.

So much for the more subjective aspect of music. As for its sensory architecture, this is quite complex. Many sense data are integrated in musical experience and therefore music is not an exclusively auditory creation; it is more than a world of mere sound. The ear, the eye, muscle sense, sense of touch, vibratory sensation, breathing and its complex movements—they all partake of and work together in musical experience. Music enters our consciousness through several portals; nevertheless, the ear is the presiding sense organ. Hence, music is the art of time integration par excellence.

Among the ancillary sense organs the eye plays an exceedingly important role; just think how essential note script is. Music as we know it in our culture would be impossible without note script, very much as language in the sense of our culture would be impossible without the written word. The score facilitates the integration of visual and auditory components of musical experience. The score is a spatial representation of auditory impressions as they happen in objective time. The fact that we can write music down on paper is one piece of evidence that music happens not only in subjective time but also in objective time. A music score is a scientifically accurate picture of the manner in which melody, harmony, and rhythm progress in objective time, much as a graph of heart action, made in the physiological laboratory, is an accurate picture of the functioning of the heart. There is a difference, however—the graph of heart action represents precisely and efficiently how the heart functions in objective time, but the note picture does not portray how music progresses in subjective time. The note picture only suggests our musical experience.

To illustrate this point, let us consider how rhythm is portrayed by a score. One of the most familiar examples of rhythmical activities is walking. A note picture of walking shows a series of identical notes, separated by equal intervals of clock time. Though it is correct from the objective, spatial, visual angle, such a note picture does not bring to light our subjective awareness of this rhythm for the very simple and obvious reason that the right foot is more important to us than our left foot. Hence, we distort subjectively the exact symmetry of the right-left rhythm as it happens in objective time.

The score indicates how notes succeed each other in objective time, but musical rhythms are ever so slight distortions of the note picture. Rhythms which pound out accurate time intervals, such as the rhythms of trains, planes, machines, clocks, put us to sleep; they do not hold our interest. Only rhythms which deviate from absolute equality of intervals in clock time keep us spellbound. Even the machine-like rhythm of jazz must be slightly irregular and uneven, so that it is not really like a machine.

The bar lines in the score divide music up into equal time intervals, but the musician plays across the bar lines by phrasing a melody. In phrasing he does not cling literally and precisely to the written score; he now prolongs this note, then he cuts the time value of another note. He brings out the meaning of the melody by distorting its mathematical time structure. Phrasing is probably one of the most important artistic means by which the musician breathes life into the dead structure of music as it exists in objective time. It is impossible to make music with a metronome ticking away, because this instrument stakes off equal intervals of clock time and this equality prevents phrasing. Principally by phrasing, and also by numerous other means, the musician elevates music as it exists in objective time and as it is congealed in the score, onto existence in subjective time.

Music is a most promising field for the study of the time problem because here we can approach this problem from several angles. The direct, intuitive, introspective approach reveals to us the subjective meaning of musical experience as it unfolds in subjective time. The indirect, intellectual, extraspective approach goes over the detour of inspection of the score which permits us to see how music happens in objective time. The complex body movements of the musician playing his instrument can be studied with mechanistic methods, including slow-motion photography. However, these movements are of a hybrid, mechanical as well as purposive nature; therefore we must keep in mind, by introspection of our own purposive movements and by empathy with other people's purposive movements, that mechanistic methods do not reveal the purposive nature of purpose-striving movement. Music then permits the study of the time problem from the viewpoints of introspection and extraspection in combination with an analysis of movement.

This brief excursion into the field of music shows clearly that man exists on the two levels of objective time and subjective time and also that time and space are steadily interwoven in human experience.

In conclusion, the premise that the ear is an organ of time perception is fallacious; one is justified to say that the spatial aspect of experience dominates the visual sphere and that the temporal aspect of experience is more in the foreground in the world of sound.

4. THE TIME STRUCTURE OF MAN AND OF ANIMALS

One can illustrate the differences between objective time and subjective time by showing how animals and man respectively live in time. This comparison will bring out how complex man's time structure is. To show the relative importance of objective and of subjective time I shall compare: a dog opening a door with his paw, a monkey knocking a banana down with a stick, primitive man making an arrowhead, a violinist practicing his instrument, and a musician giving a concert. From the first to the fifth example the relation between means and goal becomes more and more indirect; the distance in time between means and goal increases, because an increasing number of only remotely related acts are put in between intended goal and consummated goal. The meaning of the words purpose, goal, intention, changes as the time structure of behavior becomes increasingly complex and the content of the word purpose becomes richer on these different levels of temporal integration.

1. There is a direct relationship between the dog's wanting to go through the door, his pushing it open with his paw, and his

passing through the door. The purposive activities of the dog are confined to the immediate here-and-now. Intended goal and its consummation are enclosed in one actual present.

2. The time relationships in the monkey's activities are a little different; he tries to reach the banana with his paw, jumps high to get it and if this does not work, he reaches his goal quite indirectly by knocking the banana down with a stick, or he may put some boxes on top of each other to reach it in that fashion. Finding a stick, manipulating boxes, is only indirectly related to seizing and eating the fruit; this behavior is quite complex compared to the dog's behavior who is capable only of a direct relationship between means and goal. Chimpanzees are able to connect quite indirectly related activities to a goal. Köhler has given them pieces of bamboo that could be fitted together to make a stick long enough to knock down a banana, suspended way up high in the cage.[19] One of his chimps looked at the situation, could not get the suspended banana with the sticks that were lying around; he apparently thought it over after several trials, and then, lo and behold, he actually fitted the pieces together and got to his goal in this very indirect manner. The movements which fit the pieces of bamboo together are quite remotely related to getting at the fruit; in this instance, the relation between intention and goal is more complex than the use of ready-made sticks or the manipulation of boxes. The detour between intention, means, and goal becomes longer and more tortuous, and in parallel, the time structure of behavior becomes more complex.

However, the difference between the behavior of the dog and of the chimpanzee is a difference in degree rather than an essential difference. Both dog and monkey remain enclosed in the actual present; the monkey is able to get to his goal over a detour and he thereby enlarges his temporal prison to greater dimensions as he places more and more indirectly related acts between his intention and his goal. Nevertheless, the animal remains enclosed within the present. The more intelligent the animal, the wider the boundary lines of his actual present. One might be tempted

[19] Wolfgang Köhler, *The Mentality of Apes,* trans. Ella Winter (New York: Harcourt Brace & Co., 1927), plate III opposite p. 128.

to express the differences between purposive pursuits of man and those of animals in quantitative terms also. However, one has to look carefully; perhaps the differences between the acts of a monkey and a dog can be conceived on a quantitative basis, but there is an essential difference between the time structure of purposive activities of animals and of man. An activity like tool-making depends not only on a longer detour between intention and goal but in addition, to complete this task, mental activities are required which are lacking in the most intelligent chimpanzee.

3. For instance, when primitive man was making an arrow-head, he visualized a future fight at a time when he was not fighting at all. Instead of waiting passively until danger was actually upon him when he might pick up any stone that would be handy, he starts to do something about it now; he chips little bits off a stone while he is safely sheltered in his cave. These tool-making hand movements are very indirectly connected with the body movements by means of which he will eventually shoot the arrow into his prey or his enemy. This is a much longer detour than the chimpanzee took who fitted pieces of bamboo together. But not only is the detour between intention, intermediate acts, and goal longer, an essentially new, temporal factor is added; the actual present when man is making tools and the actual present when he uses them are separated by long stretches of time during which he may be doing something that is utterly unrelated to tool-making or to using a tool. Only man is capable of connecting two actual presents which are discontinuous in objective time; animals cannot integrate the present with the remote future. The animal remains imprisoned in the here-and-now; man alone can mentally leap beyond the confines of the actual present into the remote, abstract future. "A monkey may on occasion use a hammer to crack some nuts . . . But unless it happens to be in his field of vision, the monkey will not conceive the idea to fetch the hammer and to use it in an appropriate setting." [20] Köhler's chimpanzee, who seemed to contemplate the very difficult task of fitting bamboo sticks together, was not thinking of a banana maybe some-

[20] G. Revesz, *The Human Hand* (Amsterdam: N.V. Noord Hollandsche Uitgevers Mij., 1941), p. 57.

where in the remote future; he merely extended his here-and-now to a more-embracing, a more-encompassing, actual present. In making tools, primitive man lifted himself out of the confines of the immediate present in which animals are irrevocably enclosed. Man alone releases himself from the temporal prison of the actual present as he plans for the remote, abstract future. The crudest tool of primitive people and the most refined achievement of modern culture have the same temporal structure—man bursts out of the boundary lines of the concrete present and the immediate future as he plans into the far, objective future. Our capability to integrate objective time with subjective time underpins our ability to think abstractly and from this integration flows our gift of imagination.

4. A violinist who practices his instrument travels a long detour before reaching his destination; these intermediate activities have very little in common with his ultimate goal which is to give a concert—tomorrow, next week, or next year. Musicians sometimes practice without making a single sound or without even touching their instrument; in contrast, think of the purgatorial sounds that singers make while practicing. Practice is the means, performance the goal; but few of the practiced movements go into the actual performance. A musician keeps up his practice, because he projects the performance in the remote, objective future. I want to relate here a truly remarkable example of an artist's ability to work in the present toward a goal which he intends to reach in the very far future. Joseph Szigeti's career as a violinist was in danger of being shipwrecked by a tuberculous lung infection which kept him for months in a sanatorium. On his request he "was granted dispensation of twenty minutes a day for his violin. Those twenty minutes became the sum and substance of his day. All morning he would lay plans for the precious interval; all afternoon he would review in his mind the work he had done." [21] This is a grandiose instance of the power of the human mind to extend the here-and-now to unbelievable dimensions. Szigeti not only condensed hours of forethought and afterthought

[21] Howard Taubman, "Philosopher on the Concert Stage," *New York Times Magazine* (December 17, 1950), p. 22.

into twenty minutes of actual practice; so much determination is unthinkable unless he were firmly convinced that some time in years to come he would be playing again as a performing violinist.

5. During a concert a violinist actualizes and consummates years and decades of his own preparatory activities as well as the stores of knowledge and know-how transmitted for centuries from one teacher to another. His own past experience and that of a very long line of predecessors reverberates in the short span of objective time, one and a half to two hours, which is the conventional time period of a concert. A mysterious fusing and intermeshing of a welter of past experience takes place during a series of precious presents during the performance, both in the performer and in his audience.

This brings us to the social aspects of the precious present. During the concert the violinist anticipates that his audience will experience emotions which are similar to his own. The listener opens his mind so that he may receive what the performer has to give, he anticipates as yet unknown emotional experiences, he, too, projects into the future in the fringe. I quote a music critic's sensitive description of what happens between a musician and his public:

> How does he, the performer, know that the audience companions him along the path of artistic discovery and adventure? He cannot provide you with scientific evidence, but he is positive that he knows when the miracle of rapport, intimate and complete, takes place between artist and listener. He listens to himself intently as he plays and he senses the responsive vibrations of the audience. When a magical recreation is taking shape under his fingers, his skin feels as if it had sprouted goose pimples. Usually the audience reacts as he does, he insists. He divines that its nerve ends are tingling. And when the music is finished, there is a breathless moment or two of profound stillness as performer and listeners emerge from the spell and he is certain that this priceless communion has occurred.[22]

The basis of interpersonal communication is mutually attuned projection into the future in the fringe. The innermost core of

[22] Howard Taubman, "The Transformation of Vladimir Horowitz," *ibid.* (January 11, 1953), p. 10.

interpersonal communication is the anticipatory attitude of both persons, of performer and listener, of giver and receiver, of active recreator and passive recreator. Interpersonal communication has the time structure of two or more interlocking, precious present moments. In short, communication occurs in subjective time.

Objective time and the precious present play different roles in human life on different socio-economic levels. The early Greek philosophers developed a crude concept of time, namely that time is identical with the periods of light and darkness that structure our daily living; this is the very first beginning of thinking about time. According to Sivadjian, these early philosophers "confused time with the succession of days and nights." [23] There is still something left of this attitude toward time in the present-day farmer; he gets up at daybreak because the cocks are crowing, there is a glimmer in the sky and his cows start to get restless. Long before the actual moment when the beginning of a new day, which is the punctiform instant when the sun appears on the horizon, is upon him, he anticipates this event because he goes by the signs in the sky, the air warming, birds starting to fly, etc. The concrete, infinitely varied experience of daybreak is much more important to him than the abstract, punctiform instant when sundisk coincides with horizon. But for the astronomer, the aviator, the sailor, this is precisely the important moment on which they base their calculations; the lives of these people are regulated by clocks because they have to determine the simultaneity of events in punctiform instants. It is significant in this connection that farmers can judge time better than city folk.[24]

The more one is submerged in living, the more one exists in subjective time and the less one is interested in objective time. It takes children quite some time to learn to read clocks and the use of them in their daily living comes even later, to the exasperation of parents and educators. Clocks are much more important in an industrial society, where man lives surrounded by inanimate objects, than in an agricultural milieu where he is submerged in

[23] Joseph Sivadjian, *Le Temps* (Paris: Herman & Cie., 1938), p. 291.
[24] Mary Stuart, *The Psychology of Time* (New York: Harcourt Brace & Co., Inc., 1925).

the slow, vague rhythms of living things. The Chinese decorated their railroad stations with painted clocks; but with China's industrialization they will undoubtedly come around to putting up real clocks, because trains and other machines must be run by the clock. The efficiency of a complex, intermeshing industrial society depends on the determination of the simultaneity of events in objective time. This is not as far-fetched as it may sound; in this country there was no uniformity and much confusion between the timetables of the different railroad companies, because there were no standards of time-measuring: "But the railroads, rather than the Congress, were the prime movers toward a sensible standard of time. In 1883 we had almost one hundred different time zones and none was clearly definable. . . . So the railroads took the matter in their own hands. Their General Time Convention adopted a definite standard of time on Oct. 11, 1883." [25] The reaction of one newspaper, the Indianapolis *Sentinel*, shows how deeply ingrained is the archaic Greek idea that time *is* the succession of days and nights: "It is a revolt, a rebellion. The sun will be required to rise and set by railroad time. The planets must, in the future, make their circuits by such timetables as railroad magnates arrange." [26]

An interesting example of concrete living in subjective time, with a concomitant disregard for objective time, is given by Landau:

> It is impossible to understand the Moslem without acknowledging his unworldly attitude to time. Whether he be a Persian, an Egyptian, or a Tunisian, time in the Western sense [i.e., objective time] means nothing to him. . . . On innumerable occasions my Moslem friends have kept me waiting for anything from one hour to several days. . . . At the same time they would have found it perfectly natural if, instead of waiting, I myself had departed.[27]

The more concretely one lives, the *closer to* subjective time one

[25] "All Was Confusion of Clocks Until the Railroads Got Together," *The Christian Science Monitor* (April 6, 1949).

[26] *Ibid.*

[27] Rom Landau, "Peace May Be in Moslem Hands," *New York Times Magazine* (April 6, 1952), p. 29.

exists; if one lives more abstractly, one exists *closer to* objective time.

The difference between the time structure of the behavior of man and of animals can be summarized thus: man synthesizes objective time and subjective time, while animals are incapable of bringing about this highly complex synthesis. This definition seems to be contradicted by several instances of complex, purposive behavior of animals; birds build nests in the spring apparently anticipating the rearing of their young; some store food in the fall as if they want to be prepared for winter's short rations. These activities seem to deliver at least some animals from the narrow confines of the here-and-now. But let us look a little closer; purposive human activities like toolmaking, the building of huts and houses, are forever changing and developing while the swallow builds its nest now in exactly the same fashion it did thousands of years ago. Purposive acts of animals lack precisely the attribute of development which is an exclusive possession of man because it depends on man's complex time structure. Animals who are hoarding food supplies in the fall seem to forecast the remote, objective future, but they will stick tenaciously and blindly to the same behavior, even if we supply them with food every winter. Here we have blind, instinctive acts which move ahead into the immediate future in the fringe of a here-and-now, disregarding the abstract, remote future of objective time. The blindness of instinct is blindness toward the future. Only man plans for the abstract future and therefore man develops since his activities in the concrete present continuously change in view of the objective, abstract future. Animals do not contemplate the remote future: they only project into the future in the fringe. This is another way of saying that animals have no imagination, that they cannot think abstractly, and therefore their behavior is fixed once and for all.

Only man's precious present straddles huge distances in objective time, only man learns from the past experience of his parents and teachers. When a mother or father bird teach their young to fly, the "lesson" remains enclosed within the immediate present and it is quite unscientific to assume that the parent bird is thinking like a human teacher, who logically and consciously foresees what he is trying to teach his student and who anticipates what the student will do with the acquired knowledge in the remote future, in examinations or in practical life. Internal and vocal speech, writing, tradition are integral parts of teaching and learning in the human sense and all these activities presuppose the time structure of objective time integrated with subjective time. The chimpanzee who fitted sticks together and used the longer stick to knock down the banana which was suspended up high in his cage thought and acted within the immediate here-and now, but neither apes nor monkeys nor any other animals have ever been known to make tools for future, abstract, possible situations beyond the immediate present. Man has the gift of speech and of abstract thinking and therefore he can actualize in a precious present his experiences which go back into the indefinite past, and if he wishes, he can plan for the remote, indefinite future. Man has tradition and man plans for the objective future; animals seem to plan for the remote future through some of their instinctive acts, but these move blindly ahead into the future in the fringe and they lack the human quality of imagination; animals do not imagine abstractly how the future may shape up. So-called planned activities of animals are quite unrelated to what may eventually happen in the objective future.

So then the time structure of purposive behavior establishes an inherent, essential difference between man and animals on a scientific, experiential basis. The lower one descends below man, the more one must doubt the existence of purposive behavior and the more one can explain this behavior with the causal principle, since the behavior of lower animals occurs in objective time.

This brings us back to the idea of stratification in time. One cannot express this idea in neat schemata because the time structure of man and of animals is quite complex. After we have set up the concepts of objective time and the precious present, we must qualify any clear-cut and definite statements we have made about time structure on two levels. There are many instances where organic movement does exist in objective time, e.g., reflex movement, spontaneous activity of the respiratory center, heart action, intestinal peristalsis, and there are organic movements which definitely show the structure of the precious present, like skilled finger movements: we walk toward a goal, or a tiger stalking his prey creeps toward a goal. These movements must be conceived not merely as mechanical movement from a position to another position in objective time; there is also something purposive about them, though the purposiveness of these movements is not as out in the open as in the case of skilled finger movements. In case one observes insects, the problem is even more complex. When I say: "This ant is crawling toward a goal," do I make a scientific statement, or do I, like a child, identify myself with a living organism with which I should not identify myself at all? I for one see no reason to conceive ants, amebae, fishes, lower vertebrates as purpose-striving organisms, and as existing on two temporal levels. But when one comes to rodents, the attitude toward the organism, the causal and/or teleological conception of its behavior and the decision whether these organisms exist in objective and/or subjective time, remain fluctuating and unsettled. Sometimes one is convinced that these creatures exist on two time levels, much as higher mammals, apes, and man, but in most instances one can think of them very well as sort of reflex robots, causally constituted on the level of objective time without purpose-striving tendencies.

Take your cat: she acts very much like a reflex robot. But when she comes poking her nose up to you, or touches your face with her paw, or when she holds on to your child's neck without ever showing a claw, you are soon convinced that this behavior is not purely causally determined and occurring in objective time; it is purposive, foresightful behavior and moreover, there is some degree of communication between man and animal in these instances. I am convinced that this behavior exists both on the level of objective time and the precious present and that the basic mental triad is operating in my cat. Though human beings no doubt exist both on the levels of objective time and subjective time, so many combinations on these two levels are possible that here, too, one does not get clear-cut stratification but many blurred transitions. Sometimes we are absolutely certain that we sense the functioning of the basic mental triad in a precious present [28] in ourselves and in our fellow men, and sometimes we are not so sure. In many cases of animal behavior the decision, whether or not it is proper to assume that the triad is functioning in subjective time, remains an individual decision and not a generally valid one. Often one has to leave the question: "Purposive or instinctive behavior?" open, as in the case of beavers building dams.

The physical sciences use only one time form and one set of appropriate concepts, while the observer can take only one attitude toward his object. The biologist in the restricted sense, who concentrates on the functioning of an isolated organ, will have no trouble in limiting himself to the concepts of causality and objective time and he takes an extraspective attitude; his aim is to measure vital phenomena. But as soon as he begins to visualize how the organ functions within the organism from which he has isolated it, he will think very likely that the organism is a purposive entity and now he must be on his guard against tendencies to identify himself uncritically with the organism. He must be aware, while he thinks of the organism in its entirety, that he may step from the realm of the causal world in objective time into another context, namely the teleological world in subjective time, and this shift brings up a whole cluster of related problems which do not confront the physical scientist, nor the biologist in the restricted sense. Often one cannot decide whether organic behavior occurs only in objective time, or also in subjective time, and this indecision makes us hesitate as to what concepts and what attitudes are indicated; in many cases we cannot go beyond the general conviction or intuition that there is something purposive about some vital phenomena. If I do feel that the behavior of an animal is similar to and comparable with my own behavior, if I do feel the presence of the basic mental triad, if I sense the time structure of the precious present, then teleology, introspection, and its satellites are appropriate.

With the aid of the concepts of the basic mental triad and the precious present one can stake off two areas where these concepts

[28] See the next chapter.

are applicable and where they are not. These concepts are definitely indicated in the study of human behavior, but they must be definitely excluded from the study of cells, monocellular organisms, and organs. The study of the whole animal kingdom in between these two clear-cut regions is based on a hard-to-define combination of teleology and causality, of subjective time and objective time. It is the better part of wisdom not to think in teleological terms whenever the causal principle and objective time seem sufficient to explain vital processes. Constant vigilance against unscientific identification with living organisms is necessary.

5. BASIC PROBLEMS AND TIME

All basic philosophical problems converge on the time problem. I shall enumerate only a few of those problems which are important to the biologist and which have a bearing on the demarcation of structure and function from purpose.

A. Homogeneous versus Inhomogeneous

For physical science the universe is homogeneous. When the astrophysicist measures the inhomogeneous dispersion of matter in space, he still thinks of the universe as essentially homogeneous, though quantitatively varying from place to place. In biology we have mechanical movement and purposive behavior, which is an essential and irreducible contrast rooted in the time structure of movement; mechanical movement occurs in objective time, purposive movement occurs in subjective time. There is no need for two time forms in the physical sciences which study an essentially homogeneous material.

B. Causality and Teleology

Causally constituted phenomena occur in objective time, teleological processes occur in subjective time. Thus the difference between causality and teleology is anchored on the time structure of phenomena and we get away from Aristotelian teleology, which is an instance of space-dominated thinking. Spatial structure is a-teleological; we should surrender the ingrained idea that spatial structure expresses a purpose; we should accustom ourselves to finding purpose only in those phenomena which have the structure of the precious present.

C. The Psychophysical Problem

This is one of the fundamental problems in biology and it can be restated from the viewpoint of time. It arises from the necessarily dualistic approach toward living organisms; biology in the restricted sense studies biological functions occurring in objective time, by the extraspective approach; for this branch of biology the psychophysical problem does not exist. The biologist in the wider sense, who studies phenomena occurring in subjective time and who follows the road of introspection, is always right in the midst of the psychophysical problem. From the viewpoint of time one can state this problem thus—body functions occurring in objective time are causally related; the psychic aspect of the organism occurs in subjective time and it is teleologically organized. A new avenue of approach toward a solution of the psychophysical problem may be found by deriving objective time from subjective time, by differentiating extraspection from introspection, and causality from teleology.

D. Is Nonquantitative Knowledge Scientific Knowledge?

Splitting biology up in two realms brings up the question whether biology in the wider sense is really a science, because it has to forego the measuring of vital processes which occur in subjective time. The answer to this question depends on one's definition of what science is. Natural scientists, following the leadership of Galilei, think that only quantitative knowledge is scientific knowledge and that nonquantitative knowledge is insight, art, empathy, intuition—outside the field of real science. Kant has said that a science is only a real science to the extent to which it contains mathematics. In so defining science one eliminates all those data of biology, in the wider sense, and of history which cannot be measured. Introspection, empathy, identification are denied access to the temple of science. Thus one keeps out of science that which is most intimately and vitally important to us as living human beings, namely, insight into ourselves, into our fellow men, and into higher animals as purpose-striving individuals. One relegates this knowledge to literature, art, ethics, religion or philosophy because it does not conform to the natural scientific ideal that phenomena shall be measured. One can measure only those phenomena which occur in objective time, because only they can be broken up into equal elements by point instants; thus, the biologist in the restricted sense interrupts organic movement by means of point instants in order to measure it. The monistic ideal of physical science and of biology in the restricted sense is based upon the atomistic conception of reality as a homogeneous continuum occurring in objective time, because only under these conditions can one measure. But this is a highly abstract, one-sided, and impoverished conception of the universe; after all, the realm of living things shows up all manner of heterogeneities, the most important one being the stratification in time shown by some living organisms. And since we are more intimately interested in ourselves, in our fellow human beings, and in higher animals, than in nonliving objects, it is of the greatest importance to develop biology in the wider sense into a real science and let us not deprive this branch of biology from her status as a science simply because it cannot measure purpose-striving phenomena occurring in subjective time.

Measurement has held the center of the scientific stage since the days of Galilei. This is more easily understood if one remembers that extraspection is easier to master than introspection because the former is a practical, useful approach toward the world, while the latter throws off no palpable material gain. Also, the concept of subjective time is difficult to grasp because it is much easier and again much more practical to measure movement than to feel oneself into the temporal unfolding of movement. Hence, biology in the wider sense lags behind the physical sciences and behind biology in the restricted sense, but it is imperative to design appropriate methods and concepts for the study of some living organisms in their status of hybrid, causal-teleological entities.

The dualistic approach and the duality of time concepts compel us to accept nonquantitative data within the realm of science and to abandon the ideal of the measurement of all of reality. Biology in the wider sense is definitely a science in the sense that the word *scire* embraces more than merely quantitative knowledge.

E. *Life versus Death*

The fear of death is the chief motivating force which compels us to think about our place in the cosmos and this fear makes us think, in particular, about time. We do not like to think that we may die in the fringe of a precious present and therefore we push the anticipated fact that some day we will no longer be living into the far, objective future. Elaborate metaphysical systems have been set up to dispel the fear of death. But this fear causes us to think about the remote, objective future, not about the future in the fringe. Animals do not think ahead that far; they project only in the future in the fringe and if they may seem afraid of death, it is probably safer to say that they are afraid of impending damage to their body. Often they do not appear afraid of death at all and they certainly do not bury their dead. Burial of the dead is an exclusively human custom and it points to the essential difference between the time structure of man and of animals.

Anxiety toward the future and the fear of death are much the same trend of thought as that which distorts our thinking about time and life. One can think about time without being harassed by these fears by analyzing how we and how animals live in time. This understanding may not lead to a more precise definition of life and death but it does give more meaning to these concepts. Instead of trying to define life and death, one may tentatively distinguish between two levels of living and two levels of dying, on the vegetative level in objective time, and on the purposive level in subjective time.

F. *Time and Eternity*

The concept of eternity is designed to get us out of the narrow confines of the precious present, particularly out of the oppressively short future in the fringe. The outstanding attribute of objective time is the unlimited future; the past eternal is less important for our cosmic conception and for finding our place in the history of the world and its vicissitudes. The idea of eternity is originally, that is, in childhood, represented by space without boundaries. This spatial representation is a typical childhood endeavor and most of us give up thinking about eternity spatially represented as we grow older; it becomes a sort of empty concept devoid of any representation whatsoever. In fact, few people think seriously about the problem of eternity at all. Whatever representation of eternity remains from our childhood preoccupations forces us back into space-dominated thinking about time, because the unlimited future is represented by unlimited space into which we move ahead without barriers. And so we have again time expressed in terms of space.

Our thinking about time is instigated by our fear of death and so is the concept of eternity inspired by this fear. The limitless future of objective time gives us solace from this fear because it annuls death as final and inexorable. The inclination to express time in terms of space is generated by several streams of thought: the quantitative attitude, our concern with inanimate things, the domination of the physical sciences in our industrial society, appointments which make social life possible, thinking of time as if it were limitless, expressing eternity in terms of limitless space, and, most powerful of all, the fear of death. All these streams of thought congeal in the static concept of time, which is time spatially represented. Biology in the wider sense needs a dynamic time concept like the precious present. Paradoxically, the creation of the static time concept is furthered by the two opposite concepts of the punctiform instant and eternity, because both serve the expression of time in terms of space. Eternity is represented by a limitless, unbounded line, and the punctiform instant by the geometric point which is devoid of all space.

G. Time and Values

How can we transcend the ephemeral precious present which is the time form in which we experience that which never returns? Is it really so precious if it is so perishable? It "dies as it is born." Can we reach up into the sphere of nonfading, everlasting values through a precious present? It seems as if the concept of eternity overcomes the so-called destruction of time and it seems to make indestructible values, in which we all believe, really and definitely our own. But eternity is time expressed in terms of limitless space, and who would want to embed values in the medium of space?

We do experience values in a precious present, which is discontinuous, limited, non-eternal time. Values come to life in the ephemeral precious present; though unchangeable, they are nevertheless experienced in the ever-changing present. Values are experienced in change and despite of change. This variability of our experience of the valuable belongs to the essence of this experience—when you see a piece of sculpture, hear music, feel God, this experience is always new and different, perishable, and nonstatic, it does not continue in the same way at all times; it is discontinuous experience. Because of this temporal character of the realization of the values we go through periods of religious doubt; it is why artists suffer from dead feelings in relation to their creations; why I often want to give up the work at which I am now plodding; why musicians sometimes relinquish their career in midstream. The experience of the values is essentially unstable and this discontinuity cannot be overcome by creating the concept of continuous, eternal time, which is static time. Instead, we must make our time concept more adequate to understand how we live in time. For this purpose we need a dynamic time concept. Death is not overcome through the concept of eternity, but *in* the precious present. Let us look the problems of time and values, of time and death, squarely in the face and let us not go tinkering with a concept of time expressed in terms of limitless space to escape from the precious present. This trend of thought requires the heroic attitude toward life and death.

CHAPTER SIX

THE BASIC MENTAL TRIAD AND
THE PRECIOUS PRESENT

The general concepts with which one describes and understands the world of inanimate objects are causality, space, and objective time. I have constructed two concepts by means of which we understand psychological processes going on within ourselves and in some higher animals: the basic mental triad [1] and the precious present.[2]

The basic mental triad consists of condensation of the past, the act in the present, and projection into the future. The precious present consists of a past fringe, the present with duration, and a future fringe. The basic mental triad and the precious present are related as follows: condensation takes place in the past fringe, the act is consummated in the present with duration, and projection occurs in the future fringe. The basic mental triad is the foundation of our decisions, our feelings, and of our development. It is the mainspring of our purposive movements. It is a triad in so far as we exist in time not only in the present, but also in the past and in the future. This time structure is described by the concept of the precious present.

The idea of the basic mental triad is certainly not a new concept. St. Augustine, in his furious battle with the time problem, has already said the same thoughts in medieval language that I am trying to convey in more modern terms:

> Unless in the mind which acteth all this, there be three things done. For it expects, it marks attentively, it remembers; that so the thing it expecteth, through that which attentively it marketh, passes in to

[1] Adrian C. Moulyn, "Mechanisms and Mental Phenomena," *Philosophy of Science*, 14:3 (July, 1947), 242-253.

[2] Adrian C. Moulyn, "The Functions of Point and Line in Time Measuring Operations," *Philosophy of Science*, 19:2 (April, 1952), 150.

that which it remembereth. Who therefore can deny that things to come are not as yet? Yet already there is in the mind an expectation of things to come. And who can deny past things to be no longer? But yet is there still in the mind a memory of things past, and who can deny that the present time hath no space, because it passes away in a moment? [3]

Saint Augustine touches here upon the idea that the present in which we live must have extension or duration, and that, somehow, it must encompass past and future as well.

A modern philosopher puts similar thoughts in the following words:

> We are thus forced to the conclusion that something from the present spreads back over the past, transforming the latter with new and dynamically active meaning. . . . Retroaction . . . [is] . . . the power of the present to modify the past. . . . Every present is vitally affected not only by the fact that it follows its past, but by the fact that it anticipates its future. In order to be a present it must embrace elements of its own sequelae by a certain anticipatory power peculiar to experience. This characteristic of the time of spirit may be called Prolepsis. Prolepsis then is an exact analogue to Retroaction when the relation involved is that of the future to the present. [4]

What Bowman calls Prolepsis is identical with projection in the future fringe; his concept of Retroaction is quite similar to condensation in the past fringe of a precious present.

The concepts of the basic mental triad and of the precious present can be of help in describing the difference between the world of inanimate objects and the world of purpose-striving phenomena. The basic mental triad does not operate in the world of inanimate things; the causal principle suffices as an explanatory concept in this world. Causality is a binary concept, hence cause-effect sequences are symmetrical relations which can be expressed

---

[3] Saint Augustine, *Confessions*, trans. William Watts (New York: G. P. Putnam's Sons, 1931), Bk. XI, ch. 28, p. 277.

[4] Archibald Allan Bowman, *A Sacramental Universe, Being a Study in the Metaphysics of Experience* (The Vanuxem Lectures, 1934; Princeton: Princeton University Press, 1939), pp. 356, 358.

in the causal equation—cause equals effect. The time form in which these sequences occur must itself be a binary and symmetrical modality of time: therefore, objective time is the correlated time form; the objective past and the objective future are separated by a punctiform instant and they are quantitatively equal, since both are infinite. Teleological relations are asymmetrical and so the precious present, which is their appropriate time form, is askew with a long past fringe and a short future fringe. Condensation of the past may reach back into the individual's past and into the traditional past of his teachers, while the individual projects his act into the future fringe which is the future immediately ahead for a relatively short distance. The three constituents of the triad and of subjective time are vaguely delimited over and against each other and each constituent has a different magnitude compared to the others. Teleological relationships are asymmetrical in contrast to causal relations. No punctiform instant separates, knife-sharp, past fringe from future fringe, nor does it separate condensation from projection. Therefore, teleological phenomena cannot be measured. But cause is separated from effect in a punctiform instant; therefore, this binary relationship can be expressed in mathematical equations which are binary, balancing, and symmetric.

The central aspect of the basic mental triad is the act which stands on the threshold between past and future. The act synthesizes the subjective past and the subjective future into an interpenetrating whole, which is a new emergent. Through the act we express ourselves in so far as we are particular personalities which will never return and which have never been before. In so far as we act in a precious present we actualize our potentialities and we live concretely. And yet these moments are the most ephemeral aspects of our existence. It is hardly surprising then that it is difficult to draw a word picture of the basic mental triad and the precious present, which are the expression of the most concrete and yet the most perishable aspects of our existence.

Condensation in the past fringe uses memory images which become fused and which lose their distinct outlines in this process.

Our remote and our recent past becomes condensed into an act and this condensation includes memory images which were once the actual experience of our teachers who have transmitted this experience to us. Condensation reaches back most irregularly into our own past and into the collective, transmitted, traditional past of our parents and our teachers. Hence, the past fringe is irregular. Both condensation and memory are future-attuned mental functions since they are intimately interwoven with projection into the future. In projecting our act into the future fringe we dictate by this very projection which memory images are to be condensed in the past fringe. This analysis of the act in a precious present points up that there is a distinct difference between condensation of the past and memory; memory consists of discrete, clearly formed images, while they lose their definite outlines when these memory images are condensed in the past fringe.

Let me once more point out the differences between objective time and subjective time. The objective past, e.g., yesterday from noon to 1 P.M., starts and stops in two punctiform instants, but the past fringe of a precious present is not so delimited. The punctiform instant is quite irrelevant in connection with the basic mental triad and the precious present, because condensation and past fringe reach irregularly and diffusely back into the past and they penetrate vaguely and diffusely into the act taking place in the present instant with duration. It is impossible to say precisely when past fringe and condensation stop and when the act and the present instant with duration begin. The tendency to build up our world out of neatly delimited elements bounded in space by geometric points and straight lines, and delimited in time by punctiform instants, is a deterrent to our penetrating into the essence of the basic mental triad and the precious present.

The main feature of the basic mental triad is projection into the future in the fringe. The future fringe and projection are continuous with the actual present and with the act. The subjective future *grows out of* the present and infiltrates diffusely into one's private, subjective future. I like the way Sherrington describes projection into the future in the fringe: "The act puts forth, as it were, a little bud of futurity. Then also there is lent to it something of the past." [5] Projection reaches out into the immediate future in the fringe, a few seconds or a few minutes ahead of the actual present; vague though this estimate is, one wonders if it is permissible at all to judge subjective time in terms of objective time. But this much is certain, neither past fringe nor future fringe, nor actual present with duration, start and stop in punctiform instants; these three constituents of subjective time must not be conceived as if they were juxtaposed in succession, but in the sense that they are somehow contemporaneous and interpenetrating each other.

The act in the present scans the past and uses it as if it were a reservoir from which to synthesize past and future into a new entity. The past, transmitted to us by others, becomes our very own possession in an act in a precious present. The past becomes really living and meaningful through the basic mental triad operating in a precious present.

This description of the act taking place in subjective time raises a most harassing question: If one cannot delimit the two fringes from the actual present because all three aspects of subjective time interpenetrate each other, then how can one differentiate between subjective past, actual present, and subjective future? If the fringes are continuous and in part contemporaneous with the actual present with duration, then why call them past and future fringes? Embarrassing though this question is, it really flows from the fact that objective time dominates our thinking and from the profound influence which objective time exerts in our practical, daily life. To understand the concept of subjective time one must liberate one's thinking from the concept of the before-and-after relationship of objective time, where one interval is juxtaposed and external to the next interval, much as one sector on a circle is cut off from its neighbors by two geometric points. But in subjective time past, present and future interpenetrate and are, in some hard-to-fathom manner, coexistent with each other. One has to rely on intuition to understand the concept of the precious present, and one cannot fall back on spatial schemata which can only portray elements exterior to each other. Language may be more of a barrier than an aid in describing the precious present, because language is hardly designed to render interpenetration intelligible; we use language primarily and predominantly to indicate how events and objects are juxtaposed to each other in space and in objective time. In final analysis, one must *feel into,* one must empathize with, the concepts of the basic mental triad and the precious present which are designed to express our innermost, subjective core.

Our innermost core goes beyond the realm of logic. It has often been described as the irrational within us. I am trying to fathom the irrational within us by means of the concepts of the triad and subjective time. These concepts go beyond the rules and basic tenets of logic. Logical relationships can be expressed in terms of spatial schedules, since they hold between items which are external and juxtaposed to each other, but the irrational core of our inner mental life cannot be so expressed. The basic mental triad and the precious present, designed to clinch our subjective essence, resist accurate, clear-cut verbal description. I shall try to get closer to these concepts in the next chapter, on introspection.

The future in the fringe has a meaning which is entirely different from the meaning of the abstract future of objective time, since the future in the fringe exists within the context of the basic mental triad. The future in the fringe into which the act is being projected is the concrete future; it is our most intimate possession. The future in the fringe and projection polarize the actual present and the entire act toward the future. The subjective, private future, though it is intimately experienced in our acts and our decisions, is essentially unknown, unpredictable, and dimly outlined; the future in the fringe is always threatening, sometimes more, sometimes less. The act in a precious present is always surrounded with this aura of apprehension toward the future. As it has been put by others: "The emergent is that which by definition is not only unpredicted, but unpredictable. Yet it is vitally real and defines the locus of the present or of existence." [6]

[6] David L. Miller, "G. H. Mead's Conception of 'Present,'" *Philosophy of Science,* 10:1 (January, 1943), 41.

The objective future does not have this nebulous, uncharted nature and therefore the portion of animal and human behavior which exists in objective time is devoid of the apprehension toward the future which imbues the future in the fringe. The objective future is emotionally colorless. At times, the objective future seems to have such an emotional charge; this is so because we imagine ourselves acting in a precious present in the remote, objective future, and in such contemplation of the remote future objective time is transfused by the emotional attributes of subjective time.

The triad and the precious present must not be conceived as if they were a world sufficient unto themselves and apart from causally constituted processes in objective time. There are many cross relations between the order of causality and the teleological realm. But only man is able to synthesize objective time with subjective time and causality with teleology. Only man plans for the future in objective time and projects into the future in the fringe. Planning and projection continuously intermingle; planning is unthinkable without projection. First, we plan for the objective future; then, when we feel reasonably certain that our plans are completed, we act on them in a precious present and we project our act into the future in the fringe. Our daily life is overflowing with instances when we first plan, then project, but they are so submerged and so much a matter of course that it is hard to dissect planning and projection as two distinct functions. Dramatic examples of planning and projection in exceptional situations point up much more clearly that which is happening within us in humdrum everyday existence. Take, for instance, D-day, the launching of the Normandy invasion on June 6, 1944: thirty-six months, approximately, before D-day, the military planners set this date tentatively into the future and they figured back to the then present to see if it would be possible to supply an army of invasion on that day. During these thirty-six months they worked hard to line up all the required manpower, weapons, and supplies to be available on the critical day. They worked toward and planned for an abstract date in the objective future; their attitude was relatively detached and unemotional. But when D-day was around the corner, and, even more so, on the eve of that day, an entirely different attitude toward the future took hold of the military, because now the future was no longer abstract and theoretical but was a concrete and real experience. The future now reared its threatening head. We suffer from an inherent anxiety toward the future in the fringe, an anxiety which is more or less pronounced: sometimes it is hardly felt, then again it may be overwhelming, depending on the anticipated content of the future in the fringe. We assume that the anxiety for the future on D-day flows from the thought that some factors may have been overlooked, but this is only a minor cause and a superficial, rationalized aspect of our inherent, basic fear of the future in the fringe. Factors, like the weather, which may be incalculable at present, or factors which have been overlooked are essentially calculable; they could be calculated if we had more information. This is not the case with the future in the fringe which is essentially incalculable, because it cannot be expressed in terms of space with point and line. The real basis of our anxiety toward the future is deeply buried in the impenetrable essence of the future in the fringe. Subjective time cannot be measured because it cannot be expressed in terms of space, and therefore the future in the fringe is every day and each hour of every day upon us and within us, since we constantly pour our activities into the future in the fringe of a precious present. This anxiety, this emotional tension, transilluminates the functioning of the basic mental triad.

I am trying to capture our intimate activities and experiences through the concepts of the basic mental triad and the precious present. Such an attempt runs into the peculiar difficulty that we have to be at the same time closest to our innermost self and that we must take a step aside in order to be objective about that which we sense is going on within ourselves. Besides this problem, there is our ingrained habit first and foremost to turn away from our subjective selves and to turn outward into the world of objects in space and in objective time. To understand the triad and its time structure, we have to change radically these habits of thought, these attitudes toward ourselves and toward the world about us. In daily life, in the physical sciences, and in biology in the restricted sense, our intentions and trends of thinking are outward-bound and centrifugal. Instead of this self-fleeing attitude, the biologist in the wider sense must develop an inward-bound, centripetal, introspective trend of thought. One must turn inward upon oneself and remain at the same time objective, which is a most difficult and contradictory requirement. These contradictions flow from the inherent differences between the time structure of the outside world of objects and of the inner world of the subject. To understand these two worlds we must use two sets of concepts and two divergent, opposite avenues of approach. Extraspection leads into the world of objects in objective time, introspection gives us insight into the subjective world of the basic mental triad and the precious present.

We shall understand the concepts of teleology and causality better if we correlate them with the two methods of introspection and extraspection. There is yet another way of posing the problem of the way in which causality and teleology are related; this is a more intellectual, non-experiential approach. One can define teleology by comparing it with causality and inversely. Here we come upon a peculiarity of general scientific concepts in contradistinction to, e.g., mathematical or geometric concepts. One can define a triangle as three nonparallel lines, or as a line on which one constructs two acute angles; or, again, one can define a circle as the locus of equidistant points from the center of the circle. One does not have to define either geometric concept first before one can go on to define the next, as they are quite independent from each other. The definition of the circle does not contain the definition of the triangle and inversely. But if one wants to define causality and teleology, the situation is quite different; one cannot understand, nor can one define, either concept without also understanding and defining the other. In a sense, teleology contains causality, and inversely. Yet, they are diametrically opposite principles of our understanding of reality.

Besides explaining the basic mental triad and the precious present through their status in actual experience, one can understand these teleological concepts also by contrasting them with causality and objective time. This contrast can best be brought to the fore by showing how they can be derived from each other; causality flows from the basic mental triad and objective time flows from the precious présent through a process of intellectual abstraction. We have seen in Chapter Five how objective time can be derived from the precious present; now it remains to be shown how causality can be derived from the triad. An interval of objective time is developed from a precious present by the homogenization of its duration, while the punctiform instant is derived from subjective time by its total detemporalization. A similar process of abstraction transforms the basic mental triad into the causal principle. The triad with its condensation-act-projection interpenetrating in subjective time becomes cause-effect sequence juxtaposed in succession in objective time. Condensation of the past becomes cause, which is followed by its future effect, as the condensed subjective past is projected into the future fringe. And as the two asymmetrical fringes become the symmetrical objective past and objective future, so are condensation and projection transformed into symmetrical cause-effect relations. Cause and objective past equal effect and objective future. The surface of contact between cause and effect becomes zero, even as the punctiform instant which separates past from future is compressed to zero. The derivation of causality from the basic mental triad and objective time from the precious present gives us a clearer view of the enigma of the present instant, "that little something that flies away" [7] and also of the inconceivable and unrepresentable point of interaction between cause and effect.

This process of abstraction starts in childhood; Jean Piaget has made a thorough and most enlightening study of this intellectual growth in children: "For everything happens as though the child began by attributing forces to all outside bodies and as though he only ended by finding himself the 'I' that was the cause of his own force. It must be felt as absolute, as bound up with the whole

[7] Gilbert Ryle, *The Concept of Mind* (New York: Barnes and Noble, 1949), p. 163.

universe before being understood as subjective." [8] The child lives in a world which is peopled with live forces and animistic beings; he does not differentiate as yet between the force of his own body and the resistance which objects oppose against his own muscle strength when he moves them. He lives in an animistic world where inanimate objects have their own say over him and he wants to conquer these objects, just as he has to conquer the impact of living organisms on him. There starts in childhood a process of differentiation between the I and the non-I, the self and the world around us, which goes on throughout adolescence and continues in adulthood and this process of growth crystallizes finally in the realization that the inner world of the subject is different from the outer world of inanimate objects. The very length and intricacy of this process of differentiation between living and nonliving objects causes a very gradual crystallization of the concept of teleology from the concept of causality. The child gives up his animistic world picture only very gradually and haltingly as he gains self-consciousness and as he becomes able to distinguish between himself and the world about. I remember as if it were yesterday—I must have been seven or eight years old— how I bumped into a door and kicked it in temper, but I immediately checked myself, thinking how silly it was to blame the door for the pain I felt. The confusion between teleological and causal explanation of reality has a hold on us way beyond early childhood.

The derivation of causality from the basic mental triad can help to clarify our general principles. The psychophysiological basis for this derivation of causality from teleology consists of our muscle and joint sensations; muscles pulling joints, legs pushing body forward, arm throwing a stone. First, in early childhood, there is no difference between our own body and inanimate objects, but gradually, with the differentiation of non-self from the self, we go on to differentiate between causal interactions between arm and stone, our body and the surface on which we walk; and later still, we come to see that there are causal interactions be-

[8] Jean Piaget, *The Child's Conception of Causality* (New York: Harcourt Brace & Co., 1930), p. 128.

tween objects which are entirely apart from us and with which
we do not interact at all. In the early stages of the development of
science, the interaction of inanimate things was interpreted according to the early image of our body interacting with an inanimate object; Aristotle's conception of the world of inanimate
objects was such a teleological conception. Galilei took the final
step toward the elimination of teleology from mechanics, and
now the causal principle could be expressed in the form of the
causal equation, so that mathematics became applicable in the
description of the interaction between objects. This is the final
and the ultimate stage of development of the causal principle.
Starting out from the basic mental triad operating in subjective
time, a long process of intellectual abstraction develops these sub-
ject-centered data into the mechanistic conception of the world
around us occurring in objective time. In developing causality
from the basic mental triad, and objective time from the precious
present, one progresses from concrete to abstract, from subject-
near to subject-far, from inward-bound attitude to outward-bound
approach, from introspection to extraspection, from triplicate
concepts to binary concepts, from interpenetration to juxtaposition. While triadic, mental processes are heterogeneous and intertwining, causally constituted processes are homogeneous and
separated from each other by point-instants.

I do not mean to say that one can construct the causal world in
objective time from the teleological world in subjective time, nor
that the objective world issues forth from the subjective world,
but only that the roots of the concepts of causality and of objective time lie in the basic mental triad and in the precious present.
Attempts to derive the objective world from subjective experience
lead either to panpsychism or to solipsism, both of which are unsatisfactory and extreme solutions of the problems of causality
and teleology. The world is given. The subject does not create
the world but he does form the given material of experience into
entities of unlike nature with the aid of different concepts and by
approaching the varying facets of reality with contrasting attitudes. Causal unities and teleological wholes are examples of
such dissimilar entities. The derivation of causality from teleology

is in keeping with this picture. The intellect can travel the road from concrete experience to abstract concept, but not in the inverse direction. How can the intellect bring about a filling in of abstract concepts with experiential content? The intellect forms the concepts of causality and objective time from the triad and the precious present by dropping experiential content.

Although a monistic, causal, cosmic conception has its lure for the human intellect, the dualistic picture of causality and teleology has several advantages. By deriving causality from the triad, causal connections are dementalized and the childhood, animistic conception of the world is once and for all overcome because one can show that the roots of causality lie in teleology. Also, by deriving causality from teleology, one can build a bridge between the subjective and the objective aspects of some living organisms; in other words, there is the opportunity to restate, at least, and possibly to solve, the psychophysical problem. Within the context of this book the dualistic conception clarifies the concepts of structure, function, and purpose, because the concepts of structure and function are kept within the context of the causal principle and objective time, while the concept of purpose is understood through the basic mental triad and the precious present. One ends up with two clusters of dichotomies: object and subject, causality and basic mental triad, objective time and subjective time, structure and function versus purpose, causal unity and teleological whole; correlated to these dichotomies are the two methods of approach, or the two attitudes of the observing subject—extraspection and introspection. These clusters of dichotomies fall into place if one constantly keeps in mind that the concept with which one studies the object and the attitude of the observer are prescribed by the time structure of the object.

Causality and objective time describe phenomena which are continuous and homogeneous. Phenomena like lightning and thunder are apparently discontinuous and heterogeneous; physical science conceives our discontinuous experience as a homogeneous continuum by interpolating a whole series of transitional events between the lightning we see and the thunder we hear; lightning causes a sudden but momentary rise of the temperature of the air, which suddenly expands and which equally suddenly cools off again and contracts so that a thunder clap is the result. A complex, but continuous and homogeneous chain of causal links connects the two dissimilar events, lightning and thunder. The discontinuity of first lightning, then thunder, is bridged over by intercalating between these two events the continuous and homogeneous movement of air particles. In biology we have similar intercalated cause-effect chains: I throw a stone; two very dissimilar events and objects, I and the stone, interact. These two dissimilar events are connected as follows: movement of my arm is caused by pull of muscles on bones and joints; muscle contraction is caused by shortening of muscle fibrils, which in turn is due to shortening of micelles (long protein molecules) in the fibrils; this shortening is caused by the activities of enzymes which are elicited by motor inflow from the spinal cord, regulated by central neuronal processes. The macroscopic event "I move this stone," is broken up into a number of intercalated cause-effect sequences, as the analysis proceeds from the macroscopic to the microsopic and finally to the atomic-molecular levels. Heterogeneous events are broken down into a large number of processes; these events are atomized into numerous cause-effect chains in objective time, which chains are the basis of the atomistic and homogeneous conception of reality. The bridge between dissimilar events like thunder and lightning, myself and the stone, is formed by these minute cause-effect sequences, which are the further removed from concrete experience the more they are analyzed on the atomic level. The more one abstracts from immediate experience of reality, the more reality seems to become homogeneous. From this viewpoint, reality can be atomized; this process of atomization is accomplished, to a large extent, by the point-instant, the razor which cuts reality up into discrete, equal building stones. Point-instants cut effect away from cause. This separation of cause from effect is the condition under which the causal equation holds. Therefore, this equation is applicable only to those events which occur in objective time, which is homogeneous, continuous time, expressed in terms of space.

Teleological events synthesize past and future in the present in a heterogeneous precious present through the functioning of the basic mental triad. Past, present, and future intertwine in a precious present, where the punctiform-instant is irrelevant and, therefore, teleological events cannot be cut up into homogeneous parts, juxtaposed in before-after relationships. Atoms do not interpenetrate by definition, whatever their magnitude, and teleological events cannot exist, therefore, in a causally constituted world in objective time. Causality excludes teleology just as juxtaposition in objective time excludes interpenetration in subjective time. But if one conceives teleology and subjective time as the primordial concepts, and causality and objective time as the derived concepts, then teleology does not exclude causality. Causality simply flows from a more abstract way of looking at reality, while teleology is correlated to more concrete, immediate experience of ourselves and other living organisms.

The idea of the basic mental triad fits very nicely into our usual way of thinking about our own voluntary and purposive movements; this idea verbalizes what we intuitively feel about these movements. But must we believe that purposive movements of animals are evidence of their condensing their past experience, acting in the present and projecting the act into the future? That sounds rather far-fetched and too theoretical. How can we know all this about animals? And yet, animals do strive for goals, though one must not think of this goal-striving in human terms. I think one is justified in saying that the basic mental triad operates in animals in a "twilight" fashion or in a modified version compared to the functioning of the triad in us human beings. One of the many difficulties which we encounter here is that in man the triad and planning for the future are hardly separable, always occur in conjunction, but in understanding animals one must separate these two attitudes toward the future. Animals do project into the future in the fringe, but we have no evidence to assume that they plan for the remote, objective future. Theories of animal behavior must divorce planning from the triad. Animals do synthesize past, present, and future, but not in the same way as man, who takes the remote future into this synthesis.

Much as the child gradually learns to dementalize the world of inanimate objects, we have to learn as adults to dementalize the world of living organisms to a large extent. We must school ourselves not to look for the functioning of the basic mental triad in cells, plants, organs, monocellular organisms, invertebrates; true mentation starts on an ill-defined level of evolution. One must roll teleology back from the vast majority of living organisms; purpose-striving must be attributed only to higher animals and to man. The more one looks critically at the time structure of the behavior of most living organisms, the more doubtful it becomes that the basic mental triad is operating in them. This gradual roll-back of teleology allows us to use the triad as an explanatory principle in a small area only, and if we extend this principle to the animal kingdom, it must be used in a mitigated, camouflaged version.

The concepts of the basic mental triad and the precious present crystallize the concept of purpose and delimit its use in biology. They prevent us from attributing purposiveness to spatial structure and to organic functions which occur in objective time, since only those vital processes are purposive which synthesize past and future in the present.

CHAPTER SEVEN

INTROSPECTION

Definition: Introspection is the art of looking into oneself; it is the registration of one's feelings, attitudes, inner states and processes.

So far I have described the overt aspects of purposive behavior as objectively as possible and, as it were, from the outside. However, in so dissecting purposive movements one includes tacitly their subjective aspects, namely, the internal state of the man or of the animal who is aiming for a goal in the immediate future, who projects an act in time. Projection carries with it emotional tension toward the unknown future in the fringe. The study of purposive behavior must take notice of its most essential aspect, which is tension toward the future. The method through which one studies these internal states is introspection.

Introspection raises a set of new and basic problems in biology. Scientists who study the behavior of inanimate things often show a keener insight into such basic problems than biologists themselves. This comes to one's mind when one reads in Whitehead:

> Science can find no aim in nature; science can find no creativity in nature; it finds mere results of succession. These negations are true of Natural Science. They are inherent in its methodology. The reason for this blindness of Physical Science lies in the fact that such science only deals with half the evidence provided by human experience.[1]

Whitehead points here to the need to study some sectors of reality with an approach that differs radically from the objective, quantitative methods of physical science. He seems to have in mind that in studying purposive phenomena one must use methods that are

[1] Alfred North Whitehead, *Modes of Thought* (New York: The Macmillan Co., 1938), p. 211.

appropriate for this material which is so different from mechanical phenomena observed in the physical world, for he goes on to say:

> Yet it is untrue to state that the general observation of mankind, in which sense-perception is only one factor, discloses no aim. The exact opposite is the case. All explanations of the sociological functionings of mankind include "aim" as an essential factor in explanation.—A lost dog can be seen trying to find his master or trying to find his way home. In fact, we are directly conscious of our purposes as *directive* of our actions.[2]

This direct consciousness that we are purpose-striving beings is the beginning of introspection.

Physical science looks at inanimate nature objectively and from the outside. Biology in the restricted sense follows a similar approach in studying the mechanics, physics, and chemistry of life. But biology in the wider sense, which seeks to understand goal-striving processes, must approach these, as it were, from within, subjectively and by introspection.

Reality can be studied from two points of view—an introspective and an extraspective viewpoint, depending on what type of objects one wishes to scrutinize. The objects of introspection are our internal states and they require from the observer that he turns himself inward into the inner world of the self and away from the world of surrounding objects. Extraspection is turned outward into the world of objects which surround us. Gilbert Ryle describes introspection as follows:

> The technical term "introspection" has been used to denote a supposed species of perception. It was supposed that much as a person may at a particular moment be listening to a flute, or savouring a wine, or regarding a waterfall, so he may be "regarding," in a non-optical sense, some current mental state or process of his own. The state or process is being deliberately and attentively scrutinized and so can be listed among the objects of his observation. On the other hand, introspection is described as being unlike sense observation in important respects. Things looked at or listened to, are public objects, in principle observable by any suitably placed observer, whereas only the owner of a mental state or process is supposed to be able introspectively to scrutinize it. Sense perception, again, involves the

[2] *Ibid.*, p. 213.

functioning of bodily organs, such as the eyes, the ears, or the tongue, whereas introspection involves the function of no bodily organs.[3]

When I say: "Isn't this a beautiful day," I want to draw attention not only to the objective world of sunshine and warmth and colors, of soft breezes and fragrant smells, but I also mean to describe the inner feelings of well-being, of happiness that such a day engenders within us. The inner world which is hidden in the word "beautiful" lies behind the outer world into which I go out with all my senses. We are apt to overlook the feelings which lie behind sensory perceptions through which we are embedded in the outside world and which is forever edging in on us. Extraspection is constantly in the foreground in all our doings and thoughts, and, consequently, our feeble and under-developed tendencies toward introspection are covered up. It takes a specific, determined effort to bring our internal states, which are hidden by the insistence of sense perception, to the surface and to analyze them. Extraspection covers up and crowds out introspection.

One can extrapolate introspection from two statements, one of which is predominantly extraspective, the other, mixed, intro-extraspective. When I say: "I see this pink and green scarf," I simply state that two objects are interacting; myself, the more active one, and the scarf, the more passive one; I do not make my internal states and mental processes visible. But when I say: "I see this pink and green scarf, and its color scheme gives me the creeps," I draw attention not only to the interaction between two objects, but also to my own internal reactions to the object in the outside world. Both sentences imply a complex chain of physical events: the seeing subject interacts with an object which reflects light rays; I am now directing my eyes toward it; there are two inverted images on my retinas; there is a change in the pattern of an electro-encephalogram taken from the occipital regions of my brain. But there is this difference between the two statements: the disagreeable feelings which I experience in relation to the color scheme of the object do not come into focus in the descrip-

[3] Gilbert Ryle, *The Concept of Mind* (New York: Barnes and Noble, 1949), p. 163.

tion of physical and physiological processes. The sentence: "This color scheme gives me the creeps" describes, no matter how sketchily, my internal emotional reactions to the object out there. I know about these feelings and internal reactions through introspection.

Introspection is here being used in a rather loose sense. The bland awareness that I dislike such and such a color combination, that I feel happy or sad, content or disgruntled, is hardly what one means by introspection as a scientific method of observation. This general awareness of our moods is close to awareness of self, and though it may be the beginning of introspection, this sheer awareness does not suffice to objectively study our internal states and emotions.

One way of defining a thing is by saying what it is not. Is the yogi, contemplating his navel, an introspectionist? There is undoubtedly a very strong introspective trend in the Yoga, as one can see from the following quotation: "The knower would be identical with the object, and the object would be identical with the knower. It is precisely this which the Oriental method known as the Yoga attempts to achieve." [4] Northrop goes on to describe in some detail one of the Yoga techniques for getting rid of the world of sense impressions and concludes:

> Westerners as well as orientals who have performed this experiment report that the outcome is precisely what the oriental philosophical and religious doctrines maintain. Instead of being left with nothing, as the Westerner first supposes would be the case, because of his unconscious habit of identifying the whole of nature of things with a determinate kind of thing, the report is that one is left with one of the most emotionally overwhelming, aesthetically ineffable experiences, with no sense either of self or of objects, which it is within the possibility of man to enjoy; and that even though this experience is indeterminate, it none the less has a greater emotional intensity and aesthetic ineffability and luminosity than the more determinate, differentiated experiences of the specific senses exhibit.

The yogi purposely turns himself away from the surrounding world of objects, but this does not guarantee that he is objective

[4] F. S. C. Northrop, *The Meeting of East and West* (New York: The Macmillan Co., 1947), pp. 369 f.

about his own, inner, subjective processes. His being lost from the outside world does not prove that he is trying to find out objective information about himself. This inward-turned attitude does not lead to scientific and objective knowledge and it is barren in so far as biology in the wider sense is concerned. Introspection as a scientific method must fulfill the minimum requirement that it be objective. Besides, introspection must not be pushed to the extreme point where it excludes extraspection. The biologist in the wider sense must not strive to become a pure introspectionist, he must take both the inner world of the subject and the outer world of objects into account, he must seek to strike a balance between the outward- and inward-bound attitudes since his methods flow from a mixed, intro-extraspective approach. Biologists in the restricted sense must strive to become pure extraspectionists and they must roll back introspection as much as possible, but biologists in the wider sense must combine both approaches.

Many scientists and philosophers deny that introspection is a scientific method of observation, because: (1) it does not deliver up measurable data; (2) introspection gets us involved in mutually exclusive acts and hence it is impossible; one cannot at the same time do and feel something and also introspect what one is doing and feeling; (3) it gives insight only into subjective, private states which cannot be verified by others. Let us take up these points one by one.

(1) Introspection does not deliver up quantitative data and therefore it is not a scientific method of observation. This objection against introspection rests on the conviction that all science is built on the basis of quantitative data. Consequently, biology in the wider sense, which approaches its objects through introspection, cannot become a real science because it is built on subjective, nonmeasurable experience. If it should be true that there is a biologist in the wider sense hidden within all of us, it is most necessary to nip him in the bud, so as to get rid of the nonquantitative information he is gathering about living organisms. The biologist must eliminate subjective experience, he must follow in the footsteps of the physical scientist. If a chemist who is

watching a reaction in a test tube should become aware of the inner subjective processes that are now going on within himself, he must be sure to keep these experiences in the background and out of the test results. When one makes and studies an electro-encephalogram, one naturally excludes the awareness of one's private mental processes from the interpretation of the curve. And, one argues, the biologist who studies human or animal behavior must pay attention neither to his own private subjective experience nor to that of the test person or test animal. This is the ideal of pure behaviorism which is a "psychology without psyche." The entire argument is based on the premise that whatever information introspection gives is worthless to science.

However, the inner, subjective experience of man and of some animals is precisely that aspect of their behavior which fascinates the biologist in the wider sense and there can be no doubt that introspection is the road toward insight into our own, into other people's internal states, and into the psychic life of some animals. The problem is therefore not solved by getting rid of introspection, but the question is how to make it into an objective method of observation. True, one must not expect to gain quantitative data following this method, but it does bring the emotional aspects of human behavior and of some animals into view. If one can learn to become objective while following the introspective path, biology in the wider sense can become a branch of science in its own right.

This objectivity is difficult to attain, since both the subjective, private experience of the observer and that of the object which he is studying are essential and important parts of the observational setup; the biologist in the wider sense must closely scrutinize his own internal states and those of his object. Introspection is therefore an essential tool in this branch of biology. However, introspection must not be elevated to a method all by itself, but it must always go hand in hand with extraspection. The yogi's inward-turned attitude is not the same as the introspective method of biology in the wider sense. Extraspection and introspection must be directed toward those special aspects of human and of animal behavior for the study of which they are the appropriate methods and one must constantly strive for their integration.

(2) Some psychologists and philosophers hold that introspection is impossible and even nonsensical because one cannot feel one's internal states and look at them at the same time; some of these critics hold that one can study one's internal states at best by *retro*spection. Gilbert Ryle expresses this view:

> If retrospection can give us data we need for knowledge of some states of mind, there is no reason why it should not do so for all. And this is just what seems to be suggested by the popular phrase "to catch oneself doing so-and-so." We catch, as we pursue and overtake, what is already running away from us. . . . —Retrospection, prompt or delayed, is a genuine process and one which is exempt from the trouble ensuing from the assumption of multiply divided attention; it is also exempt from the troubles ensuing from the assumption that violent agitations could be the objects of cool, contemporary scrutiny. Part then, of what people have in mind when they speak familiarly of introspecting, is this authentic process of retrospection.[5]

The controversy which is raging around introspection does not shake the fact that man, on occasion, takes a look into himself; all agree that he can look at what he has done and felt just now; some are convinced that man can look at himself while he is feeling and doing. The main point we should hold fast to is that we can be objective about ourselves and that a specific approach is needed to get information about our inner states and processes. It matters little whether one calls it introspection or retrospection.

In the defense of introspection I should say that it is perfectly possible to do something and at the same time to take a look at what one is doing and feeling. This split between the doer and the observer is precisely one of the extraordinary capacities which sets man apart from animals; man is capable of splitting himself into the looker and the doer; while man performs, he can, on occasion, observe his inner states and his external behavior. Animals, on the contrary, are simply submerged in what they are doing. Take, as an example of introspective objectivity, the professional musician—at the same time that he submerges himself

[5] G. Ryle, *op. cit.*, p. 166.

in the composition that he is now playing he also knows and hears quite objectively how his playing sounds to himself and to a listener. He is aware not only of his own feelings but also of the emotions which he arouses in his public. This split between observer and doer is by no means easy to come by, it requires countless hours of teaching, practicing, and discipline, and it is so subtle a mental process that very few nonprofessional musicians possess objectivity of performance. This very objectivity is one of the basic differences between the nonprofessional and the professional musician, actor, reader. What comes to the fore in clear-cut relief in exceptional aesthetic performances is many times repeated in a much duller and submerged fashion in everyday life. Man can say to himself and to others, while he is walking, working, speaking, painting, or playing music: "See, this I am now doing, and this is how I do it." Man can perform two activities at the same time; one, outward-bound into the world around, and the other, inward-turned, which registers his inner states and his private mental processes. Introspection flows from the exquisitely human capability of splitting oneself into the onlooker and the doer. However, though it is one of the conditions for the development of introspection, this objectivity is not identical with it.

(3) A third objection against introspection as a scientific method is that it delivers up data which cannot be verified by others. Epistemologically speaking, this is the argument against solipsism, which is indeed an untenable position and which is at most, as Rickert says, a healthy transitional stage in the development of one's philosophical thinking.[6] On the psychological side one can puncture this argument by connecting up introspection with a number of ancillary attitudes and methods which, together, make up the approach of biology in the wider sense toward some living organisms. Introspection is not paying attention exclusively to what is going on within oneself; since it is co-ordinated with empathy one takes cognizance also of the inner goings-on within other human beings. In other words, introspection is one of the pillars of interpersonal communication. Introspection need not

[6] Heinrich Rickert, *Der Gegenstand der Erkenntnis* (Tübingen: Mohr, 1921).

shut us up within ourselves; on the contrary, it opens up avenues
of approach toward our fellow men and to some higher animals.

Behind the criticism that introspection does not give us verifi-
able data lies the thought that only quantitative information can
be verified. Now one of the intrinsic features of introspective data
is that they cannot be measured. Physical scientists mean by
verification that when two scientists measure the same phenomenon, they get the same numerical results. For them, truth lies in
this identity of numbers. But is all scientific information necessarily quantitative? Is scientific truth found exclusively by measuring of phenomena? In the final analysis, one can measure a
phenomenon only if one can cut it up into identical parts by
means of geometric points and straight lines. From these conditions on which measurability rests, it follows that only phenomena
occurring in objective time can be measured and that those aspects
of organic behavior which occur in subjective time cannot be
measured. Must this eminently important aspect of nature be kept
outside the fold of science because the method by which it must
be investigated does not conform with the goal of mechanistic
natural science? This monistic viewpoint leads to a one-sided and
constricted theory of the behavior of man and of some higher
animals, because the quantitative, extraspective approach of
natural science cannot describe purposive phenomena. By developing introspection into a scientific, objective method of observation,
biology in the wider sense can construct a balanced theory of
purposive behavior.

I want to make a few remarks about literature and its method
for the sake of placing introspection into historical perspective. I
confess these remarks are controversial and superficial, yet they
are not inserted to give an opinion on literature, but only to il-
luminate introspection from yet another angle. Introspection has
been practiced in the arts and literature long before it was sys-
tematically developed into a scientific method. Even so, introspection has been slow in developing as an artistic method in
literature. Much of classical Greek literature, for instance, is
written in an extraspective vein. Take Homer's description of
Odysseus' homecoming in the *Odyssey*—the peregrinations of

Ulysses, we expect, will build up to an emotional climax in the meeting and the embrace of the hero with Penelope; but nothing of the kind happens; while Homer relates at great length Penelope's doubts and cross-examination of her husband and his description of the conjugal bed, we are told of their embrace only in a few lines and the emotional experience of the couple is lost in the welter of external occurrences. Homer describes how people meet their fate, which is a force external to man, but what goes on within man himself does not come into focus.

Many centuries elapsed before introspective moods came to the surface and began to take root in literature. Jacob Burckhardt describes how this attitude emerged during the Renaissance as an artistic method in its own right:

> In the Middle Ages the two sides of consciousness—toward the world and into man's inner self—existed in a dreamlike or half-awake state, as if both sides were covered by a veil. This veil was woven from faith, childish apprehension, and delusion; seen through this veil, the world and its history seemed exotically colored, but man knew himself only as a member of a race, of a people, of a party, corporation, family, or in some aspect of the general. This veil is blown to the four winds for the first time in Italy; an *objective* contemplation and treatment of the state and of all the things of this world in general emerges; but, at the same time, the full power of *subjectivity* comes to the surface: man becomes and knows himself as a spiritual *individual*.[7]
>
> If one collects the pearls from the entire body of Western court and chivalrous poetry of both preceding centuries, a number of magnificent premonitions and isolated descriptions of mental processes will come to the fore which, at first sight, seem to vie with the Italians for the first place. Even if one does not consider lyric poetry in its entirety and if one looks only at Gottfried von Strassburg, one gets in his *Tristan und Isolde* a picture of passion which has enduring features. But these pearls lie scattered in a sea of the conventional and the artificial and their content always remains far removed from a total objectification of man's internal and spiritual riches.[8]

[7] Jacob Burckhardt, *Die Kultur der Renaissance in Italien* (14th ed.; Leipzig: Alfred Kröner Verlag, 1925), Part II, ch. 1, p. 123.

[8] *Ibid.*, Part IV ch. 4, p. 286.

He [Dante in the *Vita Nuova*] registers, without regard for the soul itself, all the shadings of its bliss and its suffering, and he molds all this with firm determination in the most rigid form of art (the sonnet). When one reads these sonnets and canzonas carefully and alternately with them the extraordinary fragments of the diary of his youth, then it seems as if all the poets throughout the Middle Ages avoided themselves, while *he* was the first to search within himself.—The spirit and the soul take here suddenly a tremendous step toward knowing their most secret life.[9]

The introspective trend comes to full bloom with Balzac, who is one of the first creators of psychological novels. Balzac does not limit himself to describing man's vicissitudes and the external occurrences in his life, but he places far more emphasis on man's internal states, his emotional reactions, and the motivations which drive him to action. Balzac has created dozens of personality types in such a penetrating fashion that they stand life-like before one. His approach differs radically from that of the Greek story teller; the story teller takes a predominantly extraspective attitude toward his characters and subject matter, while the psychological novelist follows an introspective approach. In terms of time structure one might say that descriptive literature attempts to re-create the world in space and in objective time, while the psychological novelist brings out what is hidden within man in subjective time.

He recorded in Facinao Cane: "One single passion snatched me from my studies—but was it not really part of those studies? I began to observe the activity of the Faubourg, its inhabitants, its characters. As badly dressed as the workers of the quarter, indifferent to outward appearances, I mixed among them without their showing any reserve toward me. I could join their groups, watch them shopping, and listen to their discussions on their way home from work. Observation soon became a matter of intuition with me; I looked into their souls without failing to notice externals, or rather I grasped these external features so completely that I straightway saw beyond them. My method of observation endowed me with the capacity to share in the life of the individual in question just as he lived it; it permitted me to put myself in his place in the same way

[9] *Ibid.*, p. 289.

that the dervish in the Arabian Nights assumed the form and the soul of the people over whom he uttered his magic incantation. . . ." To whom do I owe this gift? Is it a kind of second sight? Is it a quality which by abuse can border on madness? I have never explored the sources of this power. I possessed it and I used it—that was all.[10]

Introspection is not only an essential tool of the novelist who creates imaginary human beings, but it can also be exercised in our daily living because this method uncovers hidden factors that play into our interpersonal relations, and it can tear down the obstacles which hamper these relationships. We learn by introspection how we react to our fellow men.

I want to illustrate this point by showing how introspection can be applied in two simple situations in daily life. You are stopped by a policeman. The first reaction of many people is to ask themselves: "What have I done wrong?" First, they feel guilty. Almost at the same time they become angry with the policeman, simply because he has curtailed their freedom of movement. This, then, is a reaction of guilt and anger, which is often felt quite acutely and out of proportion to the facts of the situation. It is not only interesting but also of definite practical value to know more about this incongruous emotional turmoil.

Either we let feelings of guilt and anger surge up within us and feel them die down again or we may ask ourselves why we do react in this surprisingly unreasonable fashion. To find the answer to this question, we must analyze our feelings and attitudes by introspection. This interrogation may proceed on superficial or on deeper levels of consciousness. On a superficial level we come up with the answer that we feel guilty because we have infringed upon some traffic rule or other, just now or a few hours ago. The superficial reason why we are angry with the policeman may be that he is aggressive and because he throws his weight around unnecessarily. Even in case that this is so, it is only a partial explanation of the intensity and the quality of our feelings of guilt and anger. Some of us may feel guilty though we know that we

[10] Stefan Zweig, *Balzac,* trans. William and Dorothy Rose (New York: The Viking Press, 1946), p. 29.

have not broken any traffic rules and we may become angry at a policeman who is quite friendly and perfectly decent about the discharge of his duty.

So far, our examination has followed conventional notions about human conduct and it has been guided by the reality situation; we have not uncovered the deeper reasons why we react to the policeman in the manner which I have described. Looking into the deeper levels of consciousness, you will find that the acute feelings of guilt over what you have done just now stir up old and forgotten guilt feelings concerning misdeeds which you have committed in the remote past. Guilt, generated in the present situation, is overlaid by guilt that is deeply hidden in our past and which is, in reality, quite unrelated to transgression of traffic rules. You are angry not only at the policeman because he has stopped you, but in this moment you are also angry at the second-grade schoolteacher who kept you after hours, thus preventing you from taking part in the ball game on which you had your heart set. And also at father, who punished you rather severely after you had accidentally broken a window-pane when you were four years old. The anger against the policeman grows out of proportion because much of the anger which was engendered by people who had authority over you in your early life is suddenly revived and it is heaped upon the head of the poor policeman. As soon as the acute emotional reaction dies down, you may find that you actually like the man because he may explain in a polite and friendly manner why he did stop you.

We can follow an introspective approach to bring to consciousness the factors which are involved in yet another situation. You enter a doctor's waiting room full of patients. Many people feel uncomfortable in such a situation, they want to turn around and walk out. They feel rejected and like intruders; they sense in the others, who look them up and down with staring gazes, that they are unwanted. Here again we can take a passive or an active attitude. Either we are more or less aware of our feelings and of our attitudes toward others or we become interested in the reasons why we react in this illogical manner.

The superficial reason why you feel unwanted could be that

there are no vacant chairs in the waiting room and you have to stand there conspicuously while the others are sitting down in comfort. The others may very well think: "One more patient to take up the doctor's time, he will syphon off some of the doctor's energy away from us." But if you look underneath the surface appearance, if you persevere in examining your feelings and attitudes, you will find that you regard yourself as one man against a whole pack of men. The powerful and closely knit group is dangerous to the lone and weak individual; savages sometimes kill a stranger who strays into their midst. It seems as if primitive feelings that belong to archaic tribal customs are stirring within us. Insistent introspection shows that the acute feelings harassing you in the waiting room stir up feelings which you have experienced as a child. During the first day in school we were thrown into the threatening group and we had to battle our way into their midst to become one of them; besides, we lost mother and home for a few hours. Sometimes the group is outright cruel to the new child. Long-forgotten, dormant feelings and experiences play a role in the present situation in the waiting room. Soon after the dark and troublesome feelings have abated, the wish to become part of the group takes hold. Almost simultaneous with feelings of fear and rejection we experience warm feelings toward the others as we become part of the group.

Methodical introspection is a tool which we can use to make our conduct smoother in emotion-laden life situations. If you are aware of your disproportionately strong feelings toward the policeman, you may feel quite at ease with him through the fog of anger and guilt, and you will probably handle him much better than if you were passively swayed by unreasonable emotions. If you are aware by introspection of the infantile and archaic emotions in the waiting-room situation, you may train yourself to enter with relative ease a room packed full with unfriendly people, and you may submerge into the group almost immediately because you can see your emotional reactions and attitudes in their true perspective. Introspection helps us function better, because when we understand our emotions they become less threatening, less intense, and of shorter duration. Therefore archaic, infantile, and neurotic attitudes no longer interfere with our relations with our fellow men.

Many difficulties and contradictions are inherent in self-investigation. We must allow our thoughts to roam freely over our present feelings and related memories and yet we must remain within the boundaries of the situation which we want to scrutinize. Scientific introspection holds to the subject. Introspection is not daydreaming, but we must guard against the danger that it may be degraded to daydreaming. Introspection must proceed methodically to lay bare the roots of our inner psychological processes.

This method raises another question: Is it possible to feel emotion and can we at the same time look objectively at the emotion with the mind's eye? In my opinion, the problem is not *whether* introspection is possible, but *how* it is possible. Most of us know from experience that we can emote and that we can examine the emotion at the same time. We listen to and we talk with the policeman while we are aware, in a flash of insight, of the kaleidoscopic shifting of our attitudes and emotions. Man is capable of being, at the same time, the doer and the onlooker; he can split himself into observer and object. The difficulty in accomplishing this objectivity about oneself is the chief stumbling block which makes introspection so difficult. We have to take a step aside, mentally, from the stream of inner and outer events in which we are engulfed, in order to see what attitudes we are taking toward our fellow men and how we react emotionally. Some people are incapable of creating this intra-psychic distance between themselves, the doers, and themselves, the observers; they simply behave and emote without observing themselves and they do not want to bother with registering what they feel and what their attitudes are toward their fellow humans.

One of the problems inherent in introspection is the question how to teach it to others. No such problem exists in the physical sciences which follow the extraspective approach. A physical scientist can give definite and clear-cut instructions to another scientist on how to make an extraspective observation. This is so, because the object of the observation is "out there," separate from ourselves, for everyone to see, hear, touch, or smell. The relationship between the observer and his object is easily defined, be it atom, solar system, cells, or chemical reactions in a test tube. The story of the discovery of Neptune is a fascinating example of the clear-cut nature of extraspective observation: Leverrier, at the astronomical observatory in Paris, wrote to Gallé, at the observatory in Berlin, when and where they should look for a hypothetical new planet, which was observed exactly within the limits of time and space which Leverrier had staked out. In the field of emotions and interpersonal relations the relation between observer and object are fleeting and difficult to define. Therefore, the teacher can give his student only some general and approximate instructions as to how to go about looking into himself.

Freud has tried to solve this problem by creating the method of free-association. He made his patients lie down on a couch while he kept out of their sight; he instructed them to say exactly what came into their mind, no holds barred. These are artificial means which facilitate introspection and which clear away the barriers which sidetrack us in ordinary life from noticing what is going on within ourselves. In normal life circumstances and interpersonal relationships our attention is guided by what we see and hear, but in the psychiatric interview the patient is encouraged to disregard temporarily the outer world of sensory experience and to look into his own subjective inner world. The psychiatrist helps his patient to concentrate on what he feels, on what is going on in his innermost self. The external life circumstances of the patient are important only in so far as they are the background for his private, subjective experience.

Novelists like Balzac have used introspection intuitively and for artistic purposes. Freud has developed introspection into a scientific method of studying man's inner life. He was self-conscious about the style in which he wrote his case histories because, he said, they read more like novels than like scientific reports. One of the reasons for this similarity of style is that both the psychiatrist and the psychological novelist follow the introspective approach, as each seeks to fathom man's inner life in his own way. Freud's self-consciousness about his style shows that he did not see clearly what were the methodological implications of his new approach toward neurotic patients. He was confused and inconsistent in matters of general scientific principles; though he was building up psychoanalysis as a psychological, interpersonal approach toward neuroses and psychoses, he was convinced that the couch and free-association would be abandoned as soon as biologists knew more about the abnormal chemical processes which, Freud thought, were undoubtedly going on in neurotic and psychotic patients. He said, in effect, that "the doctor with the syringe is waiting to take over from the psychoanalyst." [11] This statement implies that since only the physical sciences are real sciences, the interpersonal, introspective approach must eventually be rooted out of psychiatry, if this medical specialty is to become a true science. Freud was pleading for the destruction of the very method which he himself had created.

Introspection is, as a matter of course, the chief tool of psychotherapy and of psychoanalysis. The above description of self-analysis of simple, everyday-life situations holds true, a hundred-fold enlarged, for the doctor-patient relationship in the treatment of the neuroses and of some psychoses. But the split within ourselves and objectivity as regards our inner processes is the foundation not only of these medical specialties; many other human endeavors require a similar self-critical and objective attitude. The writer, the actor, the musician, the sculptor has to be objective about his own feelings and those he creates in others; he knows about these intra- and inter-personal relations and emotions following the method of introspection. No one is in a better position to testify to the importance of our inner subjective feelings than the psychiatrist, because he observes how much his patients suffer from disturbance of the emotions; his patients suffer from a lack of feeling, from distortion, or from overcrowding of feelings. A depressed patient will tell you that he no longer experiences the normal feelings of comfort and joy that reality has always engendered within him; depressed patients do not distort reality, but their perception of reality is empty of feeling,

[11] Sigmund Freud, quoted by Stanley Cobb in *Borderlands of Psychiatry* (Cambridge, Mass.: Harvard University Press, 1943), p. 127.

emotionally flat, and therefore meaningless.[12] The emotional tone which accompanies sensory experience and interpersonal relations stays in the background in daily living, but it is of paramount importance for the psychiatrist to be aware not only of the internal states and processes within his patient, but also to keep his own internal reactions to the patient in the limelight. The psychiatrist is an introspectionist by nature or by training, or both.

One of his aims is to teach his patients to use the tool of introspection. Some people are good introspectionists, some learn this attitude with difficulty, and some never seem to learn it. The couch method and free-association have led to remarkable discoveries about the intra-psychic forces that determine the psychoses and the neuroses. However, even if one follows these directions to the letter, they do not guarantee that the person who applies this most rigid form of introspection will for certain develop insight into his inner feelings and attitudes toward his fellow men. The results of introspection depend on many factors some of which are quite beyond our control. Women generally are more gifted in this direction than men. Educators, artists, musicians are, on the whole, good introspectionists due to their personality make-up and their training. Some people simply cannot learn to look into themselves; they live in the world of objects, they are always busy measuring things, their main interest in life is to manipulate the flow of manufactured goods through their plants or their offices. They live in the three-dimensional, spatial world in objective time, a world where feelings, attitudes, and the subtleties of true interpersonal communication count for very little. They are possessed by the outward-bound extraspective attitude which glosses over our inner subjective states. The more the outward-bound attitude hypertrophies, the more the inward-bound trend dies on the vine.

Introspection draws a number of ancillary and related attitudes in its wake; they are: empathy, identification, projection, and communication. I should like to call these the "satellites" of introspection. Together with introspection they are the specific

---

[12] V. E. von Gebsattel, "Zeitbezogenes Zwangsdenken in der Melancholie," *Nervenarzt*, 1 (1928), 275 ff.

methods of biology in the wider sense, and they make communication between biologist and his object possible. Now one must not think that introspection is the point from which the other concepts and methods seem suspended, as a chandelier hangs from a hook in the ceiling. It is far more as if introspection were the hub of a wheel from which the satellite attitudes emanate and upon which they converge. Even this metaphor will not do because it suggests the order of simultaneity and causal dependency, while introspection and its satellites are directed toward objects which occur in subjective time and which belong to the order of mutual interpenetration and teleology.

Introspection makes us aware of our own internal states; empathy is the realization that identical or similar processes are going on in our fellow men and in some higher animals. How does one feel into the other person? To understand another human being one must take an attitude which is closely related to introspection. As one "listens" in a nonauditory fashion to oneself, as one takes a "nonoptical look" at oneself, so does one open his mental ear, his mind's eye for the stirrings within the other person. Looking into oneself, or introspection, prepares one for feeling into the other person, or empathy. What does one "hear," what does one "see," what does one feel in the other person? One "hears," "sees," "feels" that the other person lives in his present out of his past and into his future. I know by empathy that the other person exists in the complex precious present. I know about myself through introspection that I do exist in subjective time. Thus, empathy and introspection go hand in hand; together they are the cornerstones of interpersonal communication. Subjective time is the medium in which empathy, introspection, and communication take place.

Empathy leads to identification. We identify ourselves with those persons or animals in whom we sense, by empathy, a mental constitution similar to, or identical with, our own. We identify ourselves totally and without reservation with people who are similar to ourselves and who live on the same level of society as we do ourselves, but identification is kept in check when we meet someone from a foreign country or an unknown culture. When one studies animals, identification must be very much curtailed. The natural, common-sense identification with animals must be checked in scientific investigations. One can detect subtle shadings in the attitudes of various people toward animals; one person will feel quite justified in identifying himself with his dog to a large extent, but someone else will look upon a dog as if it were more or less an automaton which is capable of only very limited, if any, mental processes. The former investigator feels that the dog's internal states and mental processes are very similar to our own, the latter is convinced that the dog has hardly any emotions at all and that he only gives the appearance of having intelligence. In the case of the dog it is difficult to decide which person is right, since the subjective interpretation of the animal's behavior is slanted by the attitude of the observer. One may object that the study of animal behavior can never become an objective science unless these subjective elements are eradicated. I believe the answer to this objection is twofold: one is to become aware of the subjective elements in our approach toward animal behavior and the other is to find out where these subjective elements come from —namely, from the original, unconditional identification with all living organisms in our childhood.

Empathy, identification, and communication are closely related, so closely in fact that it is hard to separate them from each other. Yet it is important to distinguish among these different mental attitudes.

Projection is to read one's own emotional reactions and thought processes, attitudes, and feelings into the observed person or animal. In psychiatric language this process is reserved for pathological mechanisms; patients project their paranoid tendencies on people in their environment. But the same process, or a similar one, takes place in everyone who observes living organisms; we intuitively project our own mental attributes onto cells and onto animals. If one looks at the marvelous work of beavers, one has a strong inclination to project the human attributes of planning and foresight onto them, but on close inspection one begins to doubt if such projection is justified. The building activities of beavers are probably no more than "blind," instinctive acts which do not take the remote future into account at all; e.g., they have been known to build dam after dam in a dry river bed.

Projection flows from identification. When studying purposive behavior of man and of animals, we must be keenly aware that we are inclined toward empathy-identification-projection-communication with all that lives; this awareness is the key to applying these attitudes where they are appropriate and to subduing or eliminating them where they are uncalled for.

Introspection and its satellites are indicated when one studies vital phenomena which interpenetrate in subjective time, namely, purposive movements and mental phenomena. Extraspection is indicated in the study of vital processes which are juxtaposed to each other in objective time. By no means all vital phenomena can be studied through the introspective approach; only the behavior of man and the higher mammals is undoubtedly teleologically organized, on occasion; only these organisms can with certainty be regarded as purpose-striving beings. Indeed, it is only a very small sector of all vital phenomena which is accessible to the methods of biology in the wider sense, which is an introspective-empathic approach.

Introspection helps us to decide in what area identification and empathy are or are not relevant, because it shows us whether or not biological phenomena occur in subjective time. In this manner one can stake off where the methods of biology in the wider sense are indicated and where they should be abandoned. Such restraint is necessary to counteract our innate feeling of unity with all that lives and our uncritical tendency to identify and empathize with all living organisms. Introspection provides the clues to the limitations of and the indications for the use of the methods of biology in the wider sense because it gives us insight into the time structure of vital processes. Thus these methods need not remain diffuse and ill-determined and the attitudes and methods of biology in the wider sense need no longer seep into the domain of biology in the restricted sense; thus the concepts and methods of biology in the restricted sense can be kept clear from contamination by teleological concepts.

Purpose no longer infiltrates structure and function. The objective, extraspective approach toward reality seeks to gain quantitative information, an ideal which Galilei expressed in the adage: "Let us measure what can be measured and let us make measurable that which cannot be measured." This is precisely the aim of biology in the restricted sense, which studies the structure and function of living organisms, and therefore introspection has no *raison d'être* in this branch of science. One weighs man, measures his height, takes his temperature, determines his plasma proteins, one describes the microscopic structure of his organs, tissues, and cells, and so on; in so doing one studies man, by following an extraspective approach, and in so far, he is conceived as a living organism that is no different from any other living organism. From this viewpoint man is an animal among animals, but we must be clear about one thing—we do not see his specifically human qualities if we follow this approach exclusively. If we want to describe man in his status of human being, introspection must round out extraspection. And if one studies the purposive behavior of animals, one must also study them both by the extraspective and the introspective approaches. The objective, extraspective method of biology in the restricted sense applies physics and chemistry to the organism; it delivers up quantitative knowledge about heart activity, about neuronal functions, about intestinal motility. But whoever is interested in the purpose-striving behavior, the emotional life and the internal states of man and of some higher animals cannot travel the road of extraspection exclusively: he must follow the path of introspection.

Objective data, such as pulse rate, filling of skin capillaries, changes of respiratory rate, etc., point toward emotional stress and strain in the test person or test animal. One assumes that graphs of pulse rate, respiration, measurement of the diameter of capillaries, etc., give us insight into the emotional life of man and of animals; however, one forgets that introspection is mixed with extraspection in the interpretation of these quantitative data. Take, for instance, the "lie detector"; in the course of the questioning of a prisoner one may apply a number of instruments which register known bodily expressions of emotional stress;

e.g., one sees that pulse rate and blood pressure readings go up when certain crucial questions are asked. It looks very much as if one has here before him, black on white, an objective record of the subjective experience of the prisoner; it looks as if we have quantitative information about what goes on within the test person. Granted that it may be possible in some cases to use the "lie detector" with some advantage, as a short cut to find out what is going on inside a person, one still must not forget that one has learned on previous occasions with co-operative test persons that they did experience certain emotions in reaction to certain questions and that they reported the upsurge of such emotions at the same time that blood pressure and pulse curves showed certain deviations. Therefore, one has relied on the introspectively gained experience of these test persons in order to correlate graph with emotional life in the first place. The curves, in so far as they are data of exclusively extraspective observation, tell us nothing whatsoever about internal states of people. The curve becomes indicative of the internal life of the test person only after he has told us that our extraspective information is related to his own introspective experience. Graphs give quantitative knowledge about the body machinery, they do not tell us about man's emotional life nor about the internal states of animals.

Quantification of experience is possible only when the object of the experience occurs in objective time, since only objective time can be measured. The time structure of internal states is that of subjective time, which is nonmeasurable time, since point and line cannot be applied to the precious present. Our knowledge about emotions, gained by introspection, cannot be treated with geometric points and lines; this knowledge cannot be projected onto a co-ordinate system, nor can it be expressed in numbers. It is believed that graphs express emotional states in quantitative terms because one overlooks the fact that introspection is the actual source of information about our internal states. Introspection seeps into extraspectively acquired data.

I can well imagine that the question will be asked: What has all this to do with biology? These thoughts may be interesting to a philosopher or possibly to a psychiatrist, but how do they concern the physiologist, the anatomist, the biochemist? I believe these problems of methods and concepts do concern all biologists. This can be brought out if one compares how behavior is being investigated on different levels of evolution, from monocellular organisms upward to invertebrates, to lower vertebrates, to higher mammals, to apes, and finally up to man. This comparison clarifies at which level teleological concepts must be rolled back and in which regions they are indicated.

Loeb has studied the behavior of amoebae from the viewpoint of pure mechanisms, in terms of tropism, i.e., from the viewpoint of causality with the exclusion of teleology. But the thought that the amoeba puts its pseudopods out for a purpose, in order to get a bacterium or a food particle, easily takes hold of our imagination. We must root out this thought by critical examination of the facts. In the first place, it is not necessary on this level of evolution to go beyond a causal explanation; but a second argument against seeing purpose-striving behavior in an amoeba cuts much deeper—there is no sense in identifying ourselves with cells or monocellular organisms, or in projecting our own propensities onto them, or in assuming that there is a faint flicker of communication between us and an amoeba; we must keep these tendencies in check because there is no evidence that the movements of the amoeba synthesize past and future in a precious present. The amoeba can be studied extraspectively, it can be conceived as a causally constituted action center existing in objective time, it is a unity of structure and function without purpose-striving attributes. It is well for us to be on our guard against the uncritical tendency to identify with monocellular organisms because such awareness clarifies our methods.

Some invertebrates display an interesting gamut of behavior:

Jennings (1906) describes the behavior of the very simple organism *Stentor* in response to an experimentally induced annoyance. The *Stentor* is attached to the substratum at the lower end of its tube. At the top of the tube are cilia or hairs that draw water containing food particles down into it. If a few drops of red ink are introduced into the water near the animal, a series of responses is initiated.

First, the *Stentor* bends to one side, avoiding the ink. Secondly, if this is unsuccessful in avoiding the stimulus, the movement of the cilia is reversed, pushing the water away instead of drawing it in. If further adjustment is necessary, a third response, of contraction into its tube, is made. If none of these responses avoid the red pigment, a fourth activity appears in which the *Stentor* releases itself from its support and floats away. This little organism has a repertory of four adjustment reactions which it makes, one after another, until readjustment is effected.[13]

It would certainly seem as if this behavior serves a purpose, namely, to get away from the red ink. In biology and according to common sense one calls purposeful that which is *useful* to the individual, and, in this sense, to get away from red ink is purposive behavior. This argument looks water-tight enough; but wait—underneath this trend of thinking looms our identification with Stentor; we would, if we were a Stentor, also finally swim away; we assume that our own attributes of foresight and learning from past experience are present in Stentor in some twilight fashion. One should question whether it is really necessary to conceive Stentor as teleologically organized, because it is very well possible to conceive such an organism as a kind of robot with chemical-mechanical mechanisms built into its structure which explain on a purely causal basis why it behaves in this seemingly purposive fashion. The quest for insight into the behavior of Stentor is limited to the question: *From* what cause does Stentor behave so and so? and not: *To* what purpose? One might retreat to the position that the structure of Stentor is purposive just as the structure of a man-made machine is purposeful, but this is no longer a scientific argument. Science must not speculate on what is not given; all that is given is a certain structure which functions in a certain way, and the only remaining question is whether or not one is justified in interpreting these functions as if they were also purposeful. In the first place, to equate purposefulness with utility leads nowhere in biology, because living nature abounds with downright harmful vital phenomena. In the second place, we must be aware of our interpreting Stentor's behavior

[13] Laurence F. Shaffer, *The Psychology of Adjustment* (Boston: Houghton Mifflin Co., 1936), pp. 113-114.

as purposeful because we identify ourselves with this invertebrate and identification is an unscientific attitude on this level of evolution. Identification is the very source of our seeing purpose-striving in Stentor's purely mechanical behavior.

Now let us jump up quite a few rungs on the evolutionary ladder: beavers are noted for their building of houses, dams, and colonies. Is this behavior purposive? Several particulars about their activities which seem purposeful are, on closer inspection, not so; they have been known to build dam after dam in totally dried-out riverbeds; it is said that their felling of trees so that they fall into the water is happenstance, because trees next to water always lean offshore and beavers will gnaw at any wood that's handy, e.g., they damage the spokes of farm wagons. If one says that the marvelous structure of their dams, their colonies, their homes is purposeful, then we must assume in this lowly rodent a kind of foresight and intelligence that is practically identical with our own. One might object that this can't be so since their brain structure is much less complex than ours; beavers have lysencephalic brains without gyri and sulci. However, this argument falls back on the premise that purposive behavior can be explained on the basis of brain structure. It seems to me, however, that this theory cannot be upheld. A much more final argument against attributing human-like foresight and intelligence to beavers is this: if one ascribes this much foresight and intelligence to them, one falls prey to our innate and uncritical tendency to identify ourselves with animals. Since the biologist's approach to the behavior of animals must be hybrid, extraspective-introspective, he must at the same time keep an open mind for the need of teleological concepts and he must also keep in check his tendency toward identification. One need not go so far as to deny that beavers have any foresight or intelligence whatsoever, but one must be extremely cautious not to think of this intelligence and foresight in human terms. One of the overriding differences between foresightful behavior of animals and of man is that animals do the same thing over and over again in the same way, while man often makes little changes and sometimes drastic changes in his purposive acts. Swallows build nests now in the identical fashion they did thousands of years ago, but man is forever trying out new designs for building his houses. This means that animals do not develop, while man does develop in the psychological sense. This lack of development shows that animal intelligence is of a different category than human intelligence.

The higher we ascend in the evolutionary scale, the more pressing it becomes to hold our tendency toward empathy and identification with animals in check. In studying apes, for instance, we must never forget that we have here an animal and not a human being before us, no matter how human-like his acts may seem. Köhler studied a chimpanzee who was able to put pieces of bamboo together in order to make a long stick to knock down a banana; these acts seem to foreshadow toolmaking. It looks as if there were a gradual transition between these intelligent and foresightful acts of primates and toolmaking by human beings. However, these acts are in no way comparable with toolmaking. In these experiments man shows the way since he poses the problem, the monkey follows suit in solving it; man is the one who thought the problem out and put it before the ape to see if the animal could solve it. It is said that some monkeys make a sort of hammock from long fibers they find in the jungle; but this making of implements is entirely species-specific, as other species of monkeys do not "ape" them. Monkeys will warm themselves over a fire that has been left in the jungle, but no monkey builds a fire. Animals do have foresight, but they do not possess human foresight which has an entirely different time structure. Animals remain shut up within the present, they do not transgress beyond the future in the fringe of an actual present. Toolmaking presupposes the specifically human time structure of objective time integrated with subjective time; animals are incapable of such integration.

In contradistinction to our tendency to identify ourselves indiscriminately with animals, we are apt to curb empathy and identification when studying primitive peoples; we say "we don't understand them," and yet we are much closer to the lowliest pygmy than to the highest and best-trained primate. We are justified in identifying ourselves with human beings but we must exercise extreme caution in identifying ourselves with animals. No prescription can be given as to how far or how short a distance we should go below man in identifying ourselves with animals. The biologist should know that the tendency to identify himself with all that lives is hidden within him, but there is no sharp line of demarcation below which we must suddenly stop identifying ourselves with animals. Much depends on one's personal taste, upbringing, personality, approach toward life in general. But this much is quite certain; there is no sense in identification with cells, whether they are part of an organism or are monocellular organisms. Therefore, the extraspective approach from below, starting out from the cell as a baseline, that is, the methods of biology in the restricted sense, are not sufficient to describe and understand the purposive behavior of higher animals and of man. This study must start out from above, with man as its ceiling; it must proceed by introspective methods and one has to operate with teleological concepts, since purposive behavior exists in subjective time.

Attitudes (introspection and extraspection), concepts (purpose and causality), and time form (precious present and objective time) are interrelated. If one keeps these three interdependent elements of scientific investigation in mind, it becomes clear why the mechanistic conception of some living organisms is incomplete. Science has been onesidedly built on extraspective experience, leaving introspection to die on the vine or to be developed by art, literature, religion, and philosophy. Notwithstanding this oversight on the part of biologists, introspection and its satellites interfere with the mechanistic conception of life, and, consequently, the basic concepts of biology in the restricted sense are marred by unrecognized but tacitly assumed teleological hypotheses. The most important teleological "adherence" (Piaget) in mechanistic biological thinking is the assumption that the structure and function of living organisms are purposeful. Such unscientific teleological hypotheses can be gotten rid of by an analysis of the time structure of organic behavior, so that one can define the concept of purpose on the basis of this time structure and one comes to the insight that one has no need for the teleology of spatial structure.

By placing the time problem plumb in the middle of the discussion, one is forced to adopt a dualistic conception of living organisms and to develop two opposite approaches toward them. The split between these two conceptions and approaches flows ultimately from the chasm: objective time versus subjective time. Vital phenomena which exist in objective time are observed extraspectively, they consist of causally related elements, juxtaposed and exterior to each other. Vital phenomena which exist in subjective time are observed introspectively, they consist of teleologically related components, interpenetrating each other.

The lack of demarcation between teleology and causality, between structure and function from purpose, is due to introspection and its satellite attitudes sneaking into the concepts and the methods of biology in the restricted sense. One ascribes purposiveness to the structure and function of organisms, of organs, tissues, and cells, since one identifies oneself with them. It requires a concentrated and special effort to keep this unscientific identification in check. Insight into introspection and into the time structure of the area where it is relevant puts us on our guard against indiscriminate introspection; this understanding restrains us from identifying ourselves with cells, organs, and organisms-insofar-as-they-are-mechanisms. By remaining constantly aware of the mixed and opposite introspective and extraspective approaches, we can unmask and overcome our innate tendency to see purposiveness in structure and function. Purpose has no place in the causal order of structure and function, an order which exists in objective time. Structure and function can be cleansed of teleological "adherences" if we learn through introspection how we ourselves exist in subjective time, and if we learn through empathy how other organisms exist in time. In this fashion, the introspective approach from above, starting out with man, meets and complements the extraspective approach from below, based on the cell.

CHAPTER EIGHT

TELEOLOGICAL WHOLE AND
CAUSAL UNITY

We must investigate the concept of purpose within a larger framework than we have built so far. This wider perspective is provided by the concept of the organism-as-a-whole, or holism. I shall aim to give a clear-cut definition of this concept. This somewhat preconceived approach narrows down the concept of the teleological whole, so that it fits only the field of human purposive acts. Therefore, biologists will probably find this description of holism too limited. On the other hand, the conventional idea of the organism-as-a-whole is so vague that it does not fit biological phenomena specifically enough, since it applies equally well to nonliving systems.

As I see it, one can construct the concept of holism on the basis of two major attributes, which are: hierarchical organization and development. These two attributes reach definite status in man only, though there may be on occasion a faint suggestion of either attribute in the behavior of animals. By comparing the organism-as-a-whole with the organism-as-a-causal-unity we can describe how the purpose-striving behavior of animals differs from the purposive acts of man. This comparison leads us to analyze the time structure of the highest levels of human endeavor.

The extraspective approach, from below, based on the cell, reveals to us the order of causal connections in the organism. The biologist in the restricted sense learns about living organisms in so far as they are causal unities. But the introspective approach, from above, starting out with man, deals with teleological entities. The biologist in the wider sense, who looks into himself and who empathizes with other human beings, learns about his objects in their quality of teleological wholes. I think that we should speak of this entity only if certain definite characteristics of behavior are present. These characteristics depend on the existence of a unique time structure of behavior which occurs exclusively in man. The heart of the definition which I shall presently propose is that a teleological whole synthesizes the two levels of objective time and subjective time. This cannot be said of purposive phenomena; they synthesize the private past and the private future in a precious present. And the causal unity, which has the structure of the before-and-after in physical time, falls entirely outside the teleological realm. One can distinguish between the causal unity, between purpose-striving phenomena, and between the teleological whole according to the manner in which they happen in time—causal unities happen in objective time, purpose-striving acts occur in a precious present, and the teleological whole synthesizes objective time and subjective time.

The vast majority of vital phenomena belong to the class of the causal unity. Although some animals are capable of purposeful behavior, they do not partake of the level of holism, since they are incapable of synthesizing physical time and psychological time. The teleological whole is the highest level of biological organization; it is restricted to man's highest accomplishments. Therefore, an analysis of the general concepts of biology must needs consider man's spiritual, value-related endeavors. This line of thought leads us far away from matters conventionally called biological, i.e., beyond the field of biology in the restricted sense.

To use the word unity in conjunction with causality and the word whole coupled with teleology may seem arbitrary and somewhat pedantic, but this use can be defended by showing that there is an essential difference between the time structure of a causal unity and that of a teleological whole. Allow me to mention once more that the business of defining general biological concepts is a matter very different from defining geometric concepts, like triangle or circle. Geometric structures can be defined more or less independently from each other, but if one wants to differentiate unity from whole, causality from teleology, one cannot define the first group of contrasts without defining the second group at the same time. The definition of the concept of the circle does not contain the definition of the triangle, but the definition of the concept of the teleological whole contains and pre-supposes, in some measure, the definition of the concept of the causal unity. The same holds true of other general biological concepts. If we define the concept of purpose, we get clearer insight, by rebound, into the concepts of structure and function. At the same time that one understands the concept of the teleological whole, the concept of the causal unity falls into place.

Atoms, the solar system, cells, organs, are causal unities without teleological properties and they are definitely not wholes. Causal unities exist both in the world of inanimate objects and in the world of living organisms, but teleological wholes exist only in the latter world. They are, however, an infinitesimal minority in the field of biology in its entirety, and speaking quantitatively, teleological wholes dwindle to almost nothing, since only man is capable of creating them.

1. CAUSAL UNITY

The biologist in the restricted sense deals with the organism in so far as it is a causal unity which exists in three-dimensional space and in one-dimensional, objective time. He dissects the organism into organ systems, organs and cells, and he shows the causal relations that exist between them and also between the organism and its environment. Examples of such organ systems are: the skeleton, circulatory system, nervous system, endocrine glands, liver. The skeleton enables the body to withstand the pull of gravity and it enables muscles to move joints; our bones and joints are one set of conditions which make erect stance and locomotion possible. However, there is no need to go beyond a causal description and to say that it is the purpose of the skeleton to make erect stance and locomotion possible.

One can study the function of the heart separate from the organism by removing the heart, and one can describe its functions in terms of a mechanical device which pumps blood through the blood vessels. In fact, one can take the heart out of a living animal and one can replace it by a pump (Carrel-Lindbergh heart).

At this point we are inveigled into teleological interpretations because a pump is a man-made, hybrid, causal-teleological entity
which we have given a certain structure, so that it can function
to fit a certain purpose which we have set for ourselves. To compare the heart with a pump and to conclude that the heart must
function for a purpose is an instance of faulty teleological speculation. The function of the circulatory organs is to distribute
blood to all the cells of the organism; the blood supply makes it
possible for these cells and organs to continue living on the vegetative level. Circulation of blood is one set of conditions which
make the continued existence of the organism as a causal unity
possible.

Similarly, the functions of the nervous system lie within the
causal realm. Take reciprocal innervation—at the same time that
an agonist, a flexor muscle, for instance, contracts, its antagonist,
a stretcher muscle, relaxes; the cause of this marvelous mechanism can be found in the nervous system which sends out stimuli
to these opposing muscle groups, which stimuli cause contraction of one group and relaxation of the other. There are many
other mechanisms embodied in the nervous system, such as the
activities of the respiratory center which cause, alternatingly, contraction and relaxation of expiratory and inspiratory muscle
groups. Similar neural mechanisms cause the right arm to swing
forward when we put our left foot out. Reciprocal innervation,
integration of the function of muscle groups, the balancing of opposite body functions are mechanisms initiated by the nervous
system. These different mechanisms forge the organism into a
causal unity of overwhelming complexity. Thus the different
parts of the body are connected with each other so that they work
together in unison, minutely attuned to each other and to the
changes in the environment.

The endocrine glands accomplish this unification of body functions by chemical means. There is a subtly balancing cause-effect
relationship between the functions of the pituitary gland and the
other glands of internal secretion. For instance, the pituitary
gland stimulates the ovary to increased production of estrogenic

hormones, but estrogenic hormones, increted into the blood stream, reach the pituitary gland and they depress pituitary activity. In this instance there is a constant flux and counterflux between two opposite functions of endocrine glands.

The liver is a chemical action system which has numerous functions; among others, the formation of glycogen from dextrose. This important mechanism regulates the blood sugar level and it is one of the factors which keep the blood sugar relatively constant. One can study the synthesis of glycogen if one takes slices of liver out of the organism and places them in appropriate solutions. This function is identical inside and outside the organism, except that it is impossible to reproduce in detail all the factors of the internal environment (*milieu intérieur;* Claude Bernard) in the laboratory. In the laboratory or inside the organism, liver function is a matter of chemistry; it lies within the realm of causality.

Cannon has coined the term "homeostasis" to summarize the collective functions of the different organ systems which are the mechanisms underlying the causal unity of the organism. This term portrays very accurately the meaning of the idea of causal unity and the concept of homeostasis becomes even more meaningful if we contrast it with the teleological whole. Homeostasis indicates that the organism remains the same, static, unity of structure and function through a certain period of time. The homeostasis of a living organism is mediated particularly through the nervous system, because, more than in any other organ, there are in the nervous system an in-and-outflow of processes which balance each other or which cancel each other out; these processes are extremely complex cause-effect sequences. The nervous system correlates the different functions of the outlying parts of the body and keeps the body in tune with its environment; thus the nervous system makes it possible for the organism to continue to exist on the vegetative level. For instance, if the temperature of the environment goes up, the nervous system sends stimuli to the sweat glands which start increased production of sweat and causes skin capillaries to dilate; these two mechanisms facilitate loss of heat so that the body temperature is kept almost constant.

At the same time, pulse rate and respiratory rate go up due to re-flex mechanisms.

All these integrating neural functions are cause-effect sequences which occur in objective time. Therefore, it is uncalled for to at-tach teleological properties to the functions of the nervous sys-tem, and, by the same token, one should keep the concept of homeostasis free from teleological connotations. Biologists seem to assume that homeostasis is evidence of the purposive organiza-tion of the body; Cannon himself speaks of "the wisdom of the body." Here, as in so many other instances, one fuses causality with teleology and one uses these concepts as if they were inter-changeable. Homeostasis explains how the organism continues to exist by keeping its internal milieu constant and by adjusting it-self to the changes in the physical environment. This constancy is effected mainly through the nervous system and the endocrine glands. In unison, these functions constitute the organism as a causal unity, but the functions of cells, tissues, organs do not ex-plain how some organisms exist as a teleological whole. Most biologists assume that the causal relations between organ systems, taken together, make up the organism-as-a-whole. I think that this reasoning is fallacious. No matter how completely one may eventually know the structure and function of organ systems, this knowledge will not add up to insight into the organism-as-a-teleo-logical-whole. Organ functions, combined into causal unities which are more complex than the functions of the isolated organ, deliver up a causal unity of a higher order, but organ functions do not explain how the organism exists as a whole. A teleological whole cannot be built up *from below,* out of cells and organs and their functions.

2. TELEOLOGICAL WHOLE

I presume that most biologists will go along with a definition of the teleological whole such as H. J. Jordan gives:

We differentiate between causes and patterns of causes. Essentially, elementary processes are causally determined, but due to the inter-action of causal processes we say that the total organism is more than a summation of its parts. The separate causal factors lose their independence, because they are able to unfold their specific actions only because of the influences emanating from the totality of the other factors.[1]

When one looks at this definition a little more closely, one can see that the concept of holism has not been defined at all. What Jordan says about the totality or the wholeness of living organisms can be said with the same right about relations that hold between nonliving systems, such as atoms or the solar system. There are patterns of causes and there is interaction between causes in the world of inanimate things, in the same way as there are such patterns and as there is such interaction in living organisms. Modern field theory in physics rests on the idea that electrons, protons, neutrons are not little worlds sufficient unto themselves, but that they interact and that the field interacts with them in a patterned fashion. Inanimate things influence each other mutually in an orderly fashion, and yet it is not patterned causal interaction we have in mind when we speak of the wholeness of a living organism. The generally accepted definition of holism as it stands today in biology is too vague and it encompasses too much. It does not express the specific idea of the holism of living beings because it flows over into a meaning that applies equally well to inanimate matter.

Coghill strikes a new note when he says:

> The vertebrate animal is an organic unity by virtue of its structure. And since function is structure-in-action, the physiological wholeness of the organism is obvious. In overt behavior the inherent unity of the organism expresses itself in what I have called the total pattern, the reality of which has been impressed upon me by an exhaustive and systematic study since 1907 of the correlation of structure and function in the development of the nervous system. This study has convinced me also, not only that structure and function are one and inseparable, but that mentation with structure and function is one of an inseparable trinity, so to speak, making up the organism-as-a-whole.[2]

---

[1] H. J. Jordan, "Causality and Totality of Biological Phenomena," *Nederlandsch Tijdschrift voor Geneeskunde,* 79:2 (June 1, 1935), 2695-2708.

[2] C. Judson Herrick, *George Ellett Coghill, Naturalist and Philosopher* (Chicago: University of Chicago Press, 1949), p. 158.

However, this trinity of structure, function, and mentation does not agree with his earlier statement about the physiological wholeness of the organism which is due to structure-in-action. Though Coghill includes mentation, or purposive behavior in his definition of holism, this definition is not satisfactory because it is carried by the concept of structure.

In order to understand the holism of living organisms, we have to make an about-face—our thinking is dominated by the concept of structure, our thinking is obsessed by the idea of space; in order to understand the organism-as-a-whole, we must learn to see how it exists in time. One can define the concept of purpose fairly accurately on the basis of a description of the time structure of purpose-striving behavior. We must do the same in the case of holism. A concept of holism which is based on the time structure of the organism-as-a-whole deviates from the conventional biological concept of holism; it holds true for only a very small sector of the world of living beings, but one gains the advantage that one gets a concept of the teleological whole which can be sharply contrasted to the causal unity; hence, it is a useful and consistent definition of holism. Inasmuch as the teleological whole synthesizes objective time with subjective time, it makes very little sense to speak of the organism-as-a-whole when one works in the anatomical, physiological, chemical, or embryological laboratory, where one studies causal unities which exist in objective time. In other words, biology in the restricted sense simply does not need the concept of holism; it gets along quite all right if it regards the organism as a causal unity.

Two attributes define the concept of holism: (1) Purposes are organized in a *hierarchy* in a teleological whole; (2) a teleological whole *develops*. Holism exists in the complex time schema of objective time integrated with subjective time.

One must start out from the concept of purpose, as the lower type concept, and which must already be defined, so that one can construct holism as the next higher type concept. This excludes holism from the world of inanimate objects and from life on the vegetative level. When biologists speak of the organism-as-a-whole, they usually mean the organism-as-a-causal-unity.

Holism goes beyond a purpose which one tries to realize in a precious present; holism presupposes a hierarchy of purposes, arranged according to those purposes which are less important and those which are more important. This introduces the notion of a scale of values into the concept of holism. Such a scale is irrelevant in the causal order.

Development is a determining attribute of holism. I use this term in a specific and very circumscribed sense. Development in this context is quite a different process than the changing of spatial structure in objective time; it does not mean embryological development, nor the gradual changes of the body configuration during the growing-up period. In so far as the organism changes in space and in objective time, it is a causal unity. Other examples of so-called development are the increase of entropy of the universe, the cooling off of the sun, geological development, all of which are changes of spatial structure taking place in objective time and which have nothing in common with the development of a teleological whole. A teleological whole develops in those rare cases where the functioning of the basic mental triad in a precious present is codetermined by the individual's past experience and his anticipating an objective, remote future, sometimes far ahead of the actual present. Development in this sense is possible only on the basis of the time structure of objective time and subjective time mutually integrated. Only within this frame can we build purposes into a hierarchy of that which is more important and that which is less important. Neither objective time alone, nor subjective time by itself is sufficient to carry a scale of values. In a precious present we are absorbed in acting, deciding, moving toward an aim, and there is no opportunity in the here-and-now to decide which of the many purposes involved are more or which are less important. The actualization of values requires not only that we act in a precious present, but also that we are able to compare long past purposes with those that one expects to actualize in the remote, objective future. Man alone possesses the capacity to contemplate the remote future and to visualize the remote past, because only man has imagination, he can speak and he can write. This is the place where man stands apart from the rest of the world of living organisms. Purely as a purpose-striving being, man is in some measure an animal among animals, because at least some of them strive for a purpose projected in the future fringe of a precious present. But man alone integrates remote, past experience with a possible, contemplated, remote future precious present in the actual here-and-now; man alone contemplates what he has done in the objective past and what he will try to do in the remote, objective future. Animals are enclosed in a precious present, man is free to roam at will in large distances of objective time because he can write, he can speak, and he has imagination. Above all, he can look objectively at himself as he was in the past, as he is in the present, and as he hopes to become in the future. All these exclusively human attributes are grafted upon the complex time structure of objective time integrated with subjective time. Within the framework of these connotations and ramifications of the concept of holism there is no sense in speaking of animals as teleological wholes.

3. HIERARCHICAL ORGANIZATION

In giving examples of holistic behavior I shall concentrate on the idea of hierarchy, because we can make this aspect of holism clear by using instances of overt human behavior. The second attribute of holism, development, is development in the psychological sense and to describe this aspect of holism one would first have to build a scientific theory of man. The reason why I discuss holism does not reach that high; I want to get the concept of purpose into definitive perspective and I want to separate the concept of purpose from the concepts of structure and function.

The idea of hierarchy comes faintly to the fore when one compares reflex shutting of the eyelids with conditioned reflex shutting of the eyelid. Reflex shutting happens regardless of what is more important or less important to the organism; there is no hierarchical relationship in this situation, since it is a cause-effect chain in the before and after of objective time. But conditioned reflex shutting of the eyelid implies that the possessor of the eye is aware, however dimly, that his eye is important to him. These relatively unconscious movements point toward a hierarchical relationship between the more and the less important.

Skilled finger movements are a particularly clear example of the hierarchical structure of human behavior. A toolmaker, for instance, may keep his body almost entirely still and he may move mostly his arms, his fingers, and his eyes; sometimes he forces his body to remain motionless while he moves his fingers with delicate precision. The entire body is subdued under the task at hand. As Yakovlev says, the movement and postures of the body are "spearheaded" onto the fingertips when we are making tools, when we are writing, or playing a musical instrument.[3] We have to control the posture of our body in order to provide a base of operations for our finger movements. Posture of body and arms are subordinated to the performance of localized and special movements of the fingers. The toolmaker, the writer, or the musician organizes the general postures and the larger movements with the local small movements according to the hierarchy of that which is more important and that which is less important. These are instances of what Kurt Goldstein calls figure-ground relationship;[4] the body and arm postures are the *ground* against which the finger movements perform a *figure*.

We can demonstrate the hierarchical relation between different parts of our body quite vividly by trying to do a task left-handedly that we ordinarily would do with our right hand. You will find that the right hand constantly wants to take over from the left hand and that the posture of the body is in discord with the movements of the left hand. To overcome inborn right-handedness in such instances you must observe how you do a task with the right hand and then you must conceive the left-handed operation as the mental mirror image of the natural movements and postures. Squeeze an orange with your left hand and you will

[3] Paul I. Yakovlev, "Motility, Behavior and the Brain," *Journal of Nervous and Mental Diseases,* 107:4 (April, 1948), 318.

[4] Kurt Goldstein, *Der Aufbau des Organismus* (The Hague: Nyhoff, 1934), p. 1.

feel that the right hand does not hold the squeezer willingly; the left shoulder must be brought with a good deal of effort into a position perpendicularly above the center of the squeezer; you have to shift the weight of the body from the right to the left foot. The entire body partakes of this skilled finger and arm movement and the entire complex set of postures and movements must be organized into a hierarchical whole in which the movements of the fingertips are most important; the movements of the forearm are quite important; the posture of the shoulder is less so and the general body posture and weight distribution are still farther in the background and least important.

However, in placing skilled finger movements in the foreground, we must not overlook the fact that when we move automatically, as in stance and in walking, the body is also divided in general postures and specialized, peripheral movements. It does seem as if here, too, we have movements which are more and those which are less important. When we walk, our legs seem more important to us than our arms; we can swing our arms comfortably or we can stick them in our pockets. But let us not be misled by appearances; as soon as we pay attention to exactly how we walk, it is amazing to notice how the experience of walking changes. If you try to think which arm swings with which leg, you may become frozen on the spot for a moment, which did happen to me once when I tried to show a Parkinsonian patient how to relearn to swing his arms. On these exceptional occasions we suddenly start to evaluate how the different parts of our body work together and we become aware of their mutual dependence, and then we experience that we subjugate posture of trunk and movements of arms to movements of the legs. In learning skilled movements and when relearning automatic movements, one evaluates the various components and postures according to the value scale of what is more and what is less important within the whole complex set of movements and postures. There is then an essential difference between inborn automatic movements and learned, skilled movements. The fact that the entire body partakes of stance and walking is no proof that the organism behaves as a whole. When we walk automatically the organism behaves as a causal unity; as soon as we consciously steer this movement we behave as a teleological whole.

One can see this difference very clearly by watching how an actor and how a nonactor walk on and off stage. The actor who controls his movements and postures voluntarily knows where he is going with each step and where he is coming from; the nonactor walks automatically. While he is performing, the actor draws the public's attention now to this, then to that part of his body; now to the face, now to his fingers, then to his foot, and so on. He accomplishes this by sometimes keeping a part of his body submerged in the general body schema and then he suddenly makes some part of his body stand out as the most important means of emotional expression at that moment.

Quite differently do automatic movements come about. While walking naturally, one does not think: "Now I must take another step," no more than one thinks: "Now I must take another breath." Walking simply happens; the young child does not learn to walk in the strict sense; the mechanisms that exist in the central nervous system are exteriorized by example and encouragement from the side of his parents. If one has the misfortune to have to relearn to walk, it is quite a different matter. Now one really learns, that is, one has to evaluate postures and movements of different parts of the body according to which are more and which are less important, and one has to forge postures and movements into a teleological whole.

In performing skilled movements we act as a hierarchically organized teleological whole in which partial movements and supporting postures are attuned to the purpose for which the individual is striving here-and-now, but in stance and in walking the body works as a causal unity in which process one cause-effect chain is just as important as any other cause-effect chain involved in the process.

The hierarchy of the purpose-striving organism-as-a-whole cannot be explained on the basis of the structure and function of the nervous system, since the nervous system is an action center within the realm of causality. True, we speak of higher and lower centers, some of which suppress and dominate the others, but unless one conceives these functions as cause-effect sequences which can be translated into quantitative relationships, one unknowingly projects teleological attributes upon the nervous system. The higher centers inhibit or facilitate activities going on on the lower levels; the meaning of inhibition is that it lessens those activities and of facilitation that it increases them.

A good example of hierarchical organization is right-handedness or left-handedness. These characteristics cannot be reduced to a quantitative relationship. Right is not numerically larger than left, but it is essentially different, expressed in terms like "dominant," "leader," "more-important-less-important," terms which indicate that there exists a hierarchy of values between right and left hand. Biologists try to reduce this difference between right and left hand to a physiological, i.e., a physical property of the left hemisphere of the brain which is supposed to explain right-handedness, and of the right hemisphere which is supposed to explain left-handedness. The idea that one hemisphere dominates the other is yet another instance of our projecting our own teleological and holistic attributes onto the structure and function of an organ.

The properties and the time structure of holism imply that it cannot exist below man. Isn't this definition too narrow? Take, for example, a squirrel who is eating a nut, hunched on his hindlegs, his tail supporting him or gracefully bent upward over his back; the forelimbs hold and turn the nut, the mouth is peeling it, and the animal spits out what it does not want. All these partial movements and postures are spearheaded upon and support the main activity, namely, eating the nut. This surely must be an instance of hierarchical organization of movement. Now the squirrel jumps from branch to branch, its body goes through one subtly undulating movement, integrated from the point of its nose to the tip of its tail. Is this movement an incredibly complex causal unity or is it a teleological whole? If we believe that the latter statement is true, then we have to admit that we compare the movements of the squirrel with our own skilled movements, and we must use the entire gamut of teleological concepts to describe the behavior of the squirrel. In the first place, it seems that physiological explanations of this behavior will become sufficient with the increasing knowledge of the structure and function of the nervous system. But underlying the physiological explanation is the implication that we project psychological, mental, human attributes onto the nervous system. Teleology slips in where it does not belong because we project these properties onto neurones and their connections in an attempt to build up the organism *from below*. But the organism-as-a-whole must be approached from exactly the opposite direction; not in ascending sequence, cell-tissue-organs-organism, but by starting out with man, by an anthropocentric approach *from above*. Neurophysiology gives a mechanistic description of the behavior of the squirrel as a causal unity; now, if we regard its behavior as a teleological whole, we must ask whether we are justified in identifying ourselves with the animal and in projecting some of our own teleological and holistic tendencies onto the squirrel. By putting the problem in this fashion, it seems obvious that it is safest to regard the behavior of animals below man as causal unities. Physiology cannot answer these questions for us because it analyzes organic movement with mechanistic methods and, therefore, does not bring the purposiveness of some movements into the picture, let alone the holism of behavior. Do animals share with us all of our attributes, or only some, or none at all? These questions cannot be settled by tests in the laboratory—in fact, it may well be true that there are no answers to these questions and that we reach here the limits of human scientific knowledge and that our only guide is intuition.

The great variety of animal behavior forces us to keep the door open for revision of initial clear-cut statements. On many occasions it seems as if the behavior of animals is hierarchically organized. A muskrat, caught in a trap, will sometimes gnaw off the paw that is caught and limp off to freedom; it looks as if it is more important to it to be running around free than to have an intact body, of which it takes such excellent care under normal conditions. It is said that the male buffaloes surround the herd of cows and calves when danger lurks; they do not run off to safety, and it looks therefore very much as if their own safety is less important to them than that of the rest of the herd. It may be true that one of the attributes of holism is present in these situations, namely, the hierarchy of purposes according to the value scale of the more important and the less important, but another attribute of holism is always lacking in animals, namely, development. Since animals remain shut up within the here-and-now, they do not develop in the human sense, because they are incapable of integrating subjective time with objective time.

From the viewpoint of approach, we must ask ourselves to what extent we should identify ourselves with the buffaloes. We project onto them our male protective instincts and our female submissive drives. Identification and projection, if in moderation, seems defendable, but we must not project our holism onto animals because they do not possess the time structure which is fundamental for the existence of holism.

The physiologist will point out that the real reason why we hesitate to call the behavior of animals teleological wholes is that the structure of their nervous system is so much simpler than our own. Rodents, such as the squirrel, have lysencephalic brains whose smooth surface contains much less grey matter than the gyrencephalic, folded brains of cats, dogs, monkeys, and man. The frontal lobes of man far outreach in size and complexity the frontal lobes of chimpanzees. The biologist in the restricted sense thinks that the entire argument against the existence of holism in animal behavior on the basis of its time structure evaporates in thin air before the knowledge of the structure and function of the nervous system and its development throughout the evolutionary scale. However, one must not forget that the nervous system, whether simple or highly complex, is the condition for, but not the cause of, the occurrence of purposive behavior and the existence of teleological wholes. One cannot derive the time structure of purposive behavior and of the teleological whole from the spatial structure of the nervous system. The nervous system, including the human brain, is a unity of structure and function causally constituted, which does not reach up to the level of the teleological whole.

Hierarchy, or the subjugation of the less important under the more important, is absent in causal unities. Atoms, the solar system, organs, cells, and most organisms in their entirety, are causal unities. The electron and the positron, the neutron and the meson are equally important parts of the atom; if any one of these constituents is missing, the atom is either another atom or it is no longer an atom. The hierarchy of the more important and the less important is irrelevant in the conception of the atom, because it is a causal unity. The sun is not more important than the planets, though it is bigger, centrally located, and the source of energy, nor is the earth more important than the other planets. We do have a deep-seated inclination to think that the earth is the most important part of the solar system, but such an anthropocentric and geocentric viewpoint has been overcome by modern science. The Aristotelian cosmic conception was teleological, anthropocentric, and geocentric. The Copernican revolution overthrew Aristotelian teleology and paved the way for a causal cosmic conception. One abandoned the thought that the cosmos is organized along the teleological differentiation of the more and the less important, and one began to study the causal connections between sun and planets without assuming that there are any hierarchical relationships between them.

A similar revolution has occurred in biology since Harvey's discovery of the circulation of the blood. In the teleological, Aristotelian system, the heart was the most important organ because of its position above the diaphragm and its relations to the other organs,[5] but when Harvey showed that the heart functions according to mechanistic principles, it was dethroned from its exceptional position. With the development of physiological methods, the teleological interpretation of living organisms was more and more eliminated. Yet, it is much more difficult to abandon the idea that living organisms are organized for a purpose than to overcome the anthropocentric, geocentric cosmic conception. The organs within an organism are causally interrelated, and one must give up the idea that any one organ, be it nervous system or en-

[5] Jules Geoffroy, *L'Anatomie et la physiologie d'Aristote* (Paris: Mulot and Henri, 1878), p. 54.

docrine glands, is more important than the others. Hierarchy is irrelevant in the conception of living organisms as it is being developed by biology in the restricted sense. Only human behavior is hierarchically organized; only man is, on occasion, a teleological whole. We are apt to think that there is a hierarchical relationship between the different organ systems; we think, for instance, that the nervous system, which guides and integrates all the functions of the body, therefore makes the body into a purposive whole; we say that circulation serves the purpose of feeding all the other organs, that the skull and the spinal column have the purpose to protect the nervous system. But these interpretations are a teleological fairy tale. The nervous system fuses the different functions of many organs into a causally constituted unity, it receives the chemical substances necessary for its continued survival on the vegetative level through the blood stream; the circulatory organs are one out of a myriad of interrelated causes which make the continued existence of the structure and function of the nervous system possible. But this is not a hierarchical relationship because such a relation does not exist between causal factors. Cause-effect relations cannot be interpreted according to the value scale of the more important and the less important.

4. DEVELOPMENT

Embryological development is dissimilar to the development of a teleological whole, which has an entirely different time structure; the structure of the embryo changes in objective time. Nor is the full-grown organism and its functions which occur in objective time a teleological whole. In other words, biology in the restricted sense deals with causal unities and not with teleological wholes.

Development of a teleological whole encompasses learning from past experience, as well as planning ahead for the remote, objective future. Learning from past experience is one of the basic conditions for development, inasmuch as the individual's past experience influences his present acts. Animals, too, learn from past experience but the past does not become explicit for them and it does not crystallize in animal mentation because animals do not speak. Man integrates the past with the present by means of language, since words bring back the past alive.

Man's actions in the present are influenced not only by his past experience; he also looks far ahead into the objective future. Man moves ahead in spurts of development because he takes the distant future into account when he acts in a precious present. True, the vast majority of people are the same persons today as they were yesterday, and they will be the same persons tomorrow; they move passively along with the stream of living within them and around them; they do not truly develop, most of the time. But in periods of personal crisis or in the face of common disaster these same people may suddenly rise to the occasion and they can accomplish acts of self-negation, heroism, and leadership that are truly meteoric outbursts of development. The potentiality to develop is present in all normal human beings.

Development is not merely change. Change is development if and only if the image of the future influences an act in a precious present. Because man can look into the distant, objective future, he develops as a person and he changes his external physical environment and his social milieu. It is easier to describe the external aspect of development than the psychological phase; therefore, I shall mention mostly the former.

Both internal psychological and external social and physical development happen in spurts. The people who set these avalanches of development in motion have a concrete vision of the distant future; they are men like Gandhi, Lincoln, Ford. Few men, indeed, apprehend the objective future imaginatively and concretely. Most of us do not look more than an hour or a day ahead of the future in the fringe of a precious present; the average person does not try to construct before his mind's eye how the future will shape up ten years from now. It is more than likely that Ford had an actual mental picture of everyone driving a car. Gandhi envisioned how self-rule would be established in India. Abraham Lincoln saw before his mind's eye what would become of this country if its unity were lost; this most important purpose made him decide to pursue the to him so obnoxious means of war.

These great men do not just daydream about the future, as most of us do; they have an actual, realistic mental picture of what they think or wish is going to happen and they act upon their image of the future. They are possessed by a leading idea that runs like a red thread through their lives and that forges and molds all their actions, feelings, and thoughts into a teleological whole.

Man plans for the distant, objective future and, therefore, man changes the face of the earth for better or for worse. Who can evaluate whether this change, this development leads to improvement or to deterioration of human life? There is no generally accepted standard by which we can measure which way of life is better or more desirable; for instance, the era of the horse-drawn carriage or the automobile era. In defining the concept of the teleological whole I want to refrain from such final value judgment. I only want to show that the great renovators, the powerful leaders make development spectacular; they exteriorize processes of development that go on, from time to time, in all of us. From the viewpoint of time both the modest development of average human beings and the spectacular, awe-inspiring development of the human giants are essentially the same process—man integrates objective time with subjective time.

Man molds his concrete external physical and social environment as well as his abstract spiritual heritage in the course of time. He also changes himself. This change is not merely a becoming different from what he was previous to the change; man develops because he reshapes his past experience into new emergents during a precious present with an eye to the far-away future.

In order to describe the concept of purpose I have used homely, everyday activities of man and of animals as examples, but to describe the concept of holism we have to look at man's highest achievements on the artistic and spiritual levels. The *Odyssey*, for instance, is a beautiful story and a marvelous whole; it seems as though it were written in one breath from beginning to end. How does the writer accomplish this? We are constantly kept in suspense, although we know right from the beginning that the hero will come out all right in the end. Every time Odysseus meets a new danger, we hold our breath until he has successfully conquered that situation. There are, of course, numerous reasons why Homer keeps us spellbound, but for our present purpose I want to point out that this tale is such a marvelous whole because while unfolding his story, the writer has at all times the entire life pattern of Odysseus before his mind's eye and each specific adventure is an expression of this pattern. Each fresh incident is subjugated to the central idea: the smart, ingenious Odysseus will eventually get out of these insurmountable difficulties by using his wit.

One sees concrete examples of holism expressed and exteriorized in many different forms in the lives of great men. Gandhi expressed his belief in passive resistance in countless ways during his lifetime, by allowing himself to be put in jail, by spinning his own cotton, and, finally, in the very last moment of his life, by forgiving his assassin. One central theme runs through this man's life which organizes it into a hierarchical whole, from his formative years when he was groping to find his specific medium of expressing this central thought through his mature years when he exteriorized this belief in words and actions to bring his idea to his people, and until his last breath when he expressed it through his magnificent gesture of forgiveness. In terms of time structure one may interpret this life pattern as follows—he found himself and his central goal in a precious present when he became aware of his mission, an idea which did not suddenly fall upon him out of thin air, but which had many forebodings and had been foreshadowed in the centuries-old tradition of his national and social environment. The idea comes to fruition and to consciousness with full impact in a precious present, and from then on, he wants to carry it out into the world of his fellow human beings in long stretches of objective time and in countless media of expression. This central idea forges his life into a hierarchical whole, since everything he does or thinks or feels or decides is imbued with this idea. The leading theme is supreme over all secondary purposes which are subjugated to it.

Another most dramatic example of this hierarchy, expressed in the highest regions of human endeavor, is Beethoven's struggle with his deafness; when he became deaf in his thirties, he seriously contemplated committing suicide, because this affliction meant the end of his career as a performing musician. But the awareness of the unborn musical ideas which he harbored within himself kept these destructive drives in check. The conviction of his mission as a composer overrode his instinctual drive toward self-destruction, because to realize these ideas and to communicate them to his fellow men in the distant future was more important than to eliminate frustration and suffering in the present moment.

The concept of holism which I have outlined makes it possible finally and definitively to separate man and animals on the basis of their time structures. The statement that animals are causal unities and that they are also purpose-striving individuals contains a contradiction which is inherent in the make-up of higher animals. The causal unity of structure and function is the substructure which makes it possible for purposive behavior to exist as a superstructure. Some higher vertebrates are undoubtedly purpose-striving individuals who, on occasion, seem to differentiate between purposes which are more important and those which are less important. Although one of the attributes of holism, namely, hierarchical organization of purposes, seems to exist in the behavior of some animals, the other attribute, which is development, is always lacking. Animals remain the same during their span of life; only man develops. Animals exist in a static fashion because they remain shut up within the here-and-now. Man has the potentiality to develop and man actually develops during periods of his life, because man can straddle huge distances in objective time within a precious present. The toolmaker makes a tool for a possible goal or need in the distant future; the artist works for decades to realize an idea; the political leader may subject himself to hunger, thirst, and imprisonment in order ultimately to carry his idea to his people. Every moment, every decision, is subjugated here-and-now to a goal which was conceived in the remote past and which he envisions as an eventual reality in the distant future. The act in a precious present is part of a huge temporal panorama which only man can create. This highly complex and exclusively human time structure is the basic condition for man's existence as a teleological whole.

To restrict holism to human behavior may seem like a preconceived and doctrinaire idea, but one does gain the advantage that the concept of holism no longer hangs in midair as an ambiguous and ill-defined biological concept; one has now a guiding principle in seeking to answer the question whether the organism behaves as a causal unity in one instance and whether the organism is a teleological whole in some of its activities. Man creates a teleological whole if one can uncover that purposes are organized into a hierarchy and if there is development as the expression of the individual's leading thought and purpose.

This stringent definition of the concept of holism not only establishes the mutual relationships between the concepts of structure, function, and purpose; this definition also underlines the essential difference which exists between man and animals. Although higher animals are capable of performing purposeful acts, they do not reach up to the level of holism, because they are incapable of synthesizing objective time with subjective time. Animals are causal unities and not teleological wholes. This sharp line of cleavage between man and animals is reminiscent of Descartes' point of view; he made a sharp distinction between man and animals because he thought that only man behaved purposefully and that animals were automatons which move mechanically. In the face of all the facts which are known about animal psychology it is impossible to deny that they sometimes behave in a purpose-striving fashion, but one must exclude holism from the animal kingdom because one or both of the attributes of holism are absent on account of the simpler time structure of animal mentation.

I have used instances of human behavior to illustrate and to define the concept of holism. This excursion is apt to cause raising of eyebrows in the camp of the biologists in the restricted sense, because this analysis of human behavior has taken us quite far away from the subject matter of conventional biology. However, such excursions are inevitable if one wants to define the concepts of structure, function, and purpose clearly and to delineate them over against each other; if one wants to get into perspective life on the vegetative level and living on the purposive levels, and if one wants to see the concept of causal unity and of the teleological whole in their mutual relationships. Biology in the restricted sense, which is a group of sciences of specialization, is not designed to gain such wider insight. One group of biologists studies sugar metabolism, another group spends many a lifetime charting the finer anatomy of the nervous system, and some study in great detail the household of the endocrine glands. This specialization is necessary because no one man can possibly know all the facts that are on record about the structure and function of various organisms; specialization is also very profitable because theoretical knowledge is applied in agriculture, medicine, fisheries, etc. But specialization does not lead to a greater coherence between and a better definition of general biological concepts, such as structure, function, and purpose, causal unity, and teleological whole. Ideally, we should first define what life is before we attempt to describe these general concepts, but one should acquiesce in the fact that it is impossible to define life; the next best alternative is to divide life into the two great realms of life on the vegetative level and purposive living. With this much clarified, one can determine where man's place is on the ladder of evolution.

Biology in the wider sense can counterbalance the specialization of biology in the restricted sense by developing scientific insight into man's time structure through an anthropocentric approach. Knowledge of man's time structure enables us to grasp the concept of the teleological whole, which concept illuminates the essential difference that exists between man and animals. This clear line of cleavage between man and animals aids in delimiting biology in the wider sense from biology in the restricted sense, since we can show that the time structure of human behavior is far more complex than and that it differs in essence from the time structure of purposive behavior of animals. Having gained insight into man's time structure, we can counteract the tendency of the concept of purpose to contaminate the concepts of structure and function.

I have tried to sum up what has been said in this chapter in the form of a table. This table, which contains only a few, widely separated stages of the evolutionary process, shows that the time structure of organic behavior becomes less complex from man downward to the primitive forms of living matter.

EVOLUTION AND TIME

ORGANISM	TIME STRUCTURE		
	Juxtaposition in Objective Time	Interpenetration in Subjective Time	Integration of Objective Time and Subjective Time
Man	Causal unity of structure and function	Purposeful behavior	Holism
Higher vertebrates	Same	Same	Problematical
Fishes, amebae	Same	Doubtful	No
Plants	Same	No	No
Cells, tissues, organs	Same	No	No

CHAPTER NINE

SUMMARY

Two leading thoughts can be discerned in the foregoing discussions, a negative one and a positive one: (1) structure and function are not purposive; (2) purposive phenomena have the time structure of the precious present. However, it has not been attempted to give a definition of life which should be, ideally, the base line from which to start out in defining structure, function, and purpose. Such definitions are usually unsatisfactory and it may well be that one can no more define life than one can define what an inanimate object is. Let us take for granted that we understand, more or less, what we mean by the term "living organism"; and from there we go on to distinguish the two levels of life—the vegetative and the purposive levels. Cells, tissues, and organs exist only on the vegetative level; so do plants, monocellular organisms, and probably also deteriorated psychotic patients. Some organisms exist both on the vegetative and on the purposive levels: man, apes, higher animals. It is impossible to determine on what level of evolution purpose-striving activities end; there is a vague area of transition, not a clear line of cleavage between these two types of behavior. Yet another distinction must be made, that between the causal unity and the teleological whole. Not all purpose-striving organisms are teleological wholes; only man is, on occasion, a holistic entity. The use of the concept of holism in this sense flows from a somewhat arbitrary, but I believe a useful, definition; holism manifests itself in: (1) a hierarchy of purposes, (2) development, and (3) integration of objective time with subjective time. Only man is capable of creating this complex time structure. This definition of holism is useful because now we have a clear line of cleavage between man and animals—though some animals are purpose-striving beings, they are never capable of all of the attributes of holism. Admittedly, the dichotomies of vegetative versus purposive life, causal unity versus teleological whole, and man versus animals do not lead to a definition of life; yet, we gain the advantage that we can define purpose over against structure and function on the basis of these dichotomies, anchored upon the concepts of objective time and subjective time.

Thus one comes to a fourfold stratification of reality: (1) Inanimate objects which exist in space and objective time; (2) some organisms which, living on the vegetative level, exist in space and in objective time; we gingerly sidestep the mystery of life in our definitions; (3) other organisms, living both on the vegetative and on the purposive levels, exist both in objective time and in subjective time; (4) man is the only organism living on the vegetative, on the purposive, and on the holistic levels; only man integrates objective time with subjective time.

Biology in the restricted sense studies the structure and function of living organisms. It shows that plants, animals, and man are made up out of the same constituents, and it shows that the same properties of protoplasm exist throughout the entire realm of living organisms. Embryology shows how much the human embryo looks like an aquatic organism at certain stages of its development; the brain of a chimpanzee has a structure and function very similar to the human brain. But the way of looking at living organisms of biology in the restricted sense is space-dominated. To get clarity in our basic biological concepts we must get into focus the differences between man and animals which flow from the time structure of our own and of animals' behavior. Certainly, Köhler's chimpanzee fitted pieces of bamboo together, he made a tool if you will; two geese "help" their wounded mate off the ground; male buffaloes protect the herd; beavers behave as if they were engineers; bees make geometrically precise honeycombs, etc. But where is the animal who speaks, writes, makes tools for future use, teaches his young activities which are totally useless at the moment, buries his dead, makes useless objects of art, fights and dies for an abstract, unpractical idea? The answer to these questions can be found, at any rate in part, in the differences between the time structure of man and of animals—animals remain shut up in the here-and-now, man bursts out of the confines of the precious present. Man synthesizes objective time and subjective time in his holistic activities, which cannot exist without this time structure.

Against this background one can define structure, function, and purpose. The relations between structure and function are usually conceived as bilateral, and therefore both concepts are utterly vague and undefined. Does structure determine function or inversely? Does a giraffe have a long neck because it eats leaves from trees, or does its reaching up high cause its neck to be long? One tucks something like a causal relationship away in the word "determine," but underneath this causal connection lurks a teleological interpretation of the relation between structure and function. We think that the length of the giraffe's neck must serve a purpose, as we think that the structure of our hand serves the purpose of grasping things between thumb and fingers. We compare the hand and many other organs with tools, and so we glide into the teleological interpretation of function. Instead we should think of the structure and function of an organ as a complex causal network; given this structure and function we can sometimes use it for certain purposes. This way of looking at the organism sets the concept of purpose apart from the description and explanation of the structure and function of organisms.

Unless we keep purpose separate from structure and function, the relation between structure and function does not come to a standstill. Much confusion is caused by the fact that muscles hypertrophy due to use, which seems like a clear-cut instance of function determining structure; if you use a muscle often enough, its tone improves and its size increases. But this is hardly enough evidence to prove that function causes certain structures. The structure and function of the muscle are given and all that happens is that muscle fibers enlarge a little bit with exercise and that there is more tonic nervous inflow. Here is only a quantitative change, but nothing is intrinsically changed in the function and structure of the nerve-muscle-bone apparatus. If, on the other hand, one holds that structure determines function and that the two are causally connected, then the relation between them becomes clear-cut: function is mechanical movement caused by or-

ganic structure. But this unidirectional relation between structure and function does not become clear until one has defined the
concept of purpose, so that one can see that there is nothing
purposive about structure. If one learns to understand organic
structure as a very complex set of spatial relations without teleological admixtures, then one can roll Aristotelian teleology back
from biology in the restricted sense, as it has been eliminated
from the physical sciences. Structure causes function; structure
and function together are the condition for, but not the cause of,
purposive phenomena. Purpose exists only in those organic movements which interpenetrate in a precious present.

Structure and function are ubiquitous biological concepts, but
purpose is a markedly restricted concept. Purpose fades out of
existence below man; there is no sharp line of demarcation below
which there are no longer purposive phenomena. Behavior of
insects, though it appears to be mechanical movement in the
majority of cases, can give evidence of foresight and changeability
on occasion, which may be evidence that it is more than mechanical cause-effect sequences. The Peckhams have observed such
deviation from apparently fixed behavior in certain wasps. Mr.
and Mrs. Peckham have made an experiment with a certain wasp
species, which insect displays a remarkable ritual while moving
its prey into its nest. After killing the prey, this wasp pulls it to
the entrance of the nest and leaves it there. The wasp crawls into
the nest empty-handed, but presently it comes up again, fetches
the prey and drags it down into the nest. The Peckhams inter-
fered with this ritual; they waited until the wasp was underground and moved the prey a little distance away from the
entrance of the nest; then, when the wasp came up, it scampered
about until it found the prey, pulled it back to the entrance,
dropped it there and went down without its prey. The Peckhams
moved it again and again and as many times the wasp went down
into its nest without its prey. With each repetition of the experiment the impression is reinforced that the ritualistic behavior of
this insect is rigidly fixed. However, after repeating the experiment more than two hundred times, the Peckhams observed
that the wasp took its prey to the entrance of the nest, did **not**

leave it there, but, instead, pulled it immediately underground. The behavior of this wasp, which is fixed under normal conditions, was changed under the conditions of this experiment.[1]

Phenomena like these make it impossible to press all organic behavior into clear-cut schemata and to know in all instances whether a phenomenon is purposive or not. Life is a mystery both on the vegetative and on the purposive level. Vegetative vital phenomena can be studied with the ready-made methods of the physical sciences, adapted to this specific material, while living on the purposive level must be approached with a set of new and nonmechanistic concepts which are being developed into a scientific system only in the last fifty years.

Structure and function are based on the cell. Biology in the restricted sense builds up a mechanistic conception of the organism as it exists in objective time starting out from below, with the cell. This is a space-dominated conception. Purpose, defined on the basis of the time structure of certain organic movements, is a markedly restricted concept which has a ceiling—man—but which has no floor, since it becomes increasingly uncertain below the level of higher animals whether or not some vital phenomena are purposive. On one hand, purpose becomes more accurately defined, from the viewpoint of time, but on the other hand, it is applicable only in a relatively vaguely delimited area. This state of affairs can be partially remedied by defining the concept of the teleological whole in such a manner that holism flows from synthesis of objective time with subjective time; therefore, holism is confined to man. Purpose has a ceiling but no floor, holism has both a ceiling and a floor. It seems better to define these concepts in a preliminary and admittedly unsatisfactory fashion rather than to use purpose interchangeably with structure and function, and the teleological whole interchangeably with causal unity. Before all things we must get away from seeing purposiveness in the spatial structure of organisms. Teleology can be rolled back from structure if one sees purpose only in movements which are characterized by interpenetration in subjective time. Purpose is re-

[1] George W. Peckham and Elizabeth W. Peckham, *Wasps, Social and Solitary* (Westminster: Archibald Constable & Co., 1905), pp. 304-305.

leased from spatial structure and is established on the basis of
the time structure of movement.

The study of vegetative vital phenomena follows the extraspective approach of the physical sciences. Purposive movement requires of us that we assume an introspective attitude. In line
with the thoughts of Kurt Goldstein, one might call these approaches "from below" and "from above":

> As I see it, up to now, all attempts to understand life have taken the
> road from "below upward." Convinced that the classes of living be-
> ings constitute a scale on the lower rungs of which are living organ-
> isms of relatively simple structure and functions, and that the
> higher ones are distinguished from the lower ones only by virtue of
> an increasingly greater differentiation, one has tried to investigate
> processes of the "lower ones" first, as being the "simpler ones," and
> to ascend from them to the analysis of the "higher and more com-
> plex organisms."—Basically, the viewpoint that the lower living be-
> ings are the simpler ones and that it is simpler to study them has
> determined the procedure of research "from below upward."—The
> following exposition of vital phenomena takes the opposite direc-
> tion. It begins with man and it seeks to understand the behavior of
> other living organisms from that vantage point.[2]

"From below upward" is the extraspective, objective approach
of biology in the restricted sense and it leads to quantitative
knowledge about vegetative, mechanical vital phenomena. The
opposite approach "from above downward" is the introspective,
anthropocentric approach of biology in the wider sense and it
leads to insight into purposive processes. Since purposive behavior is always connected with causally determined structure
and function of an organism, one can never separate biology in
the wider sense and its introspective approach from biology in
the restricted sense and the extraspective method. If one should
try to get by with introspection only, one is not a scientist but a
mystic or a yogi or one who is losing contact with reality. If one
should try to rid biology entirely from introspection, one is likely
to find all manner of introspective data tucked away in facts

[2] Kurt Goldstein, *Der Aufbau des Organismus* (The Hague: Nyhoff, 1934),
p. 1.

which are ascertained by extraspection. The balanced viewpoint is to stake off these two fields, their methods and their goals against each other, and never to lose sight of the fact that all of us biologists are studying the living organism, be it from different viewpoints and with different methods. The time structure of vital phenomena has the final say as to which approach is indicated in the study of a particular group of vital phenomena. Introspection and extraspection are not irretrievable contrasts, since they can be made to harmonize with each other through an analysis of the time structure of biological phenomena.

This trend of thinking leads to a dualistic conception of the world, because the underlying premise is that purposive movement differs in essence from mechanical movement. This difference is based on the schism between objective time and the precious present. Monism flows from the premise that purposive movement is a complex variety of mechanical movement and that one does not differ essentially from the other. Sensori-motor reflexes are simplest; conditioned reflexes are more complex, and purposive movements are most complex cause-effect chains according to the monistic explanation of the behavior of all living organisms. The neural mechanisms underlying purposive movements are so complicated that these movements are unpredictable, and therefore we are inveigled into thinking that they form a class by themselves, that they are "free," or "voluntary," or "purposive." Monism postulates the existence of mechanical movement only, it uses the causal principle and the concept of objective time, it follows only the extraspective approach and it admits only quantitative data as scientific; it derives all organic movement from the structure and function of the nervous system. At bottom we fool ourselves when we say that we are purpose-striving beings, we make believe that we transcend causality. Beyond causality and quantification lies the nebulous field of mysticism, of speculation and of phantasy. The monist forces the unification of all organic movement under the heading of mechanical movement by postulating that the nervous system is teleologically organized. Actually, these are not monistic theories because teleological elements are injected into the structure and function of the nervous system, unbeknown to the scientist. Teleology is tucked away as contraband.

The dualist counters this trend of thinking with the following argument: purposive movement is not a complicated version of mechanical movement; it is a modality of movement which forms a separate class, since it occurs in subjective time, while mechanical movement occurs in objective time. It is difficult indeed to differentiate between these two modalities of movement, since they coexist and intertwine. Mechanical organic movement does occur separately from purposive movement, but purposive movement does not exist without the simultaneous presence of mechanical movement. One needs teleology, subjective time, and the introspective approach to understand the intimate nature of purposive behavior. Scientists who deny that introspection is, or can ever become, a scientific method of observation overlook the fact that there are two types of organic behavior. The advantage of the monistic theory seems to be that the clarification of the relation between nervous system and purposive movement simply awaits further advancement of our knowledge of the structure and function of the nervous system. The disadvantage of the dualistic theory is that it keeps us on edge because it leaves the relations between nervous system and purposive behavior shrouded in darkness. The roots of this unsatisfactory state of our knowledge are deeply buried in the time structure of movement; neural mechanisms which occur in objective time are instances of the atomization of organic functions with point-instants, but purposive movements which occur in subjective time do not start and stop in point-instants and therefore they cannot be so atomized. Consequently, there cannot be a causal relationship between neural mechanisms in objective time and purposive movement in subjective time. What then is this relationship? This is the burning question which is kept alive by the riddle of the psychophysical problem.

The monist thinks that the dualist deceives himself with his introspective data which he cannot measure. The dualist deplores that the monist who refuses to travel the road of introspection is blind to the most important aspects of his own behavior, which is purposive movement.

The introspective approach and the use of teleological concepts leads eventually out of the field of biology in the wider sense and over into art, ethics, philosophy, metaphysics, and religion. Therefore, the biologist in the wider sense must have some awareness, however vaguely outlined, of metaphysical questions. The biologist in the restricted sense has no use for metaphysical speculations; and whether he believes that the world is made up of inanimate matter and is a grandiose sort of a machine or whether he thinks that matter is ultimately of a "spiritual" nature makes little difference in the actual pursuit of bringing to light causal relationships within organisms and between organism and environment. But whoever deals with purposive phenomena will ask himself somewhere along the road of his investigations: What is the ultimate purpose of life, i.e., of human life? Experience does not answer this question. The biologist in the wider sense must see the purposes which he describes in a hierarchical relationship, and how is he going to differentiate the more important from the less important goals unless he has some sort of a value scale with some ultimate purpose at the top of the hierarchy? I do not suggest that the biologist in the wider sense must have a ready-made metaphysics, but he must at least be aware of the metaphysical problems with which he comes in close contact, since the approach from above starts out with man.

Psychiatry in particular overlaps with metaphysics because it is building toward a theory of man. But biology in the restricted sense which sets out to paint a huge cosmic panorama in the theory of evolution also skirts around and often comes into conflict with established religious and philosophical-metaphysical conceptions of the universe and theories about the "purpose" of human life. Here the word "purpose" has an entirely different connotation than when one speaks of the purpose of this or that movement of man or animal. If biologists see more clearly that they are likely to transgress the field of philosophy and religion because they are bound to use the concept of purpose, then they will be less likely to make irresponsible statements about these human endeavors which lie on the boundaries of biology in the wider sense. This awareness may do away with some of the useless haggling that is going on between religion and psychiatry; if biologists have at least an inkling that they constantly touch upon metaphysical problems, then the concepts of structure, function, and purpose fall into line.

Purpose on the level of biology in the wider sense is part of a hierarchy of purposes. This hierarchy has a baseline in purposive movement of animals and of man and it reaches its most exalted point in the spiritual values of art, ethics, logic, philosophy, and religion. The introspective approach, from above, with man, is bound to infiltrate upward into metaphysical theories of human life. Therefore, if purpose be differentiated from structure and function, biology can aid in the building up of a scientific theory of man.